JANE'S 1983-84
AVIATION REVIEW

JANE'S 1983-84
AVIATION REVIEW

edited by Michael J.H. Taylor

Third year of issue

JANE'S

First published in the United Kingdom in 1983 by
Jane's Publishing Company Limited
238 City Road, London EC1V 2PU

Distributed in the Philippines and the USA and its
dependencies by
Jane's Publishing Inc,
135 West 50th Street,
New York,
NY 10020

ISBN 0 7106 0285 5

Designed by Geoffrey Wadsley

Printed in the United Kingdom by
Netherwood Dalton & Co Ltd,
Huddersfield, Yorkshire

Contents

Introduction

Hercules transports and Phantom fighters at Royal Air Force Stanley, Falkland Islands. (*Aviation Photographs International*)

This edition of *Jane's Aviation Review* incorporates changes in style and content designed to increase the number of illustrations and differentiate between the topical features and the *Chronology, New aircraft of the year* and *Jarrett's jubilees*, which appear each year. A further innovation is the introduction of photo features, including one on the Paris Show. As usual, the contributions are from some of the best informed and most respected writers in the field of aerospace.

The last edition of the *Review* was dominated by the conflict over the Falkland Islands. Since the fighting ended there have been many questions asked about the future of the islands and Britain's role in it. Can and should Britain meet the expense of "Fortress Falk-

lands"? Is Argentina now reconciled to a negotiated settlement? To the islanders there is no doubt that Britain is spending scarce defence resources wisely by retaining land, sea and air forces in the South Atlantic, and this view appears to be shared by the majority of Britain's public and politicians, at least in the short term. The most wasteful aspect of the policy is the air link between Ascension Island and Stanley, involving the extensive use of flight-refuelling tankers. Although the past months have seen the appearance of the RAF's "new" VC10 K2 tanker aircraft, with ex-British Airways TriStars to come, the problem remains critical. The present British Government believes that the only realistic answer, if Fortress Falklands is to continue, is to construct two runways for big jets near Fitzroy. Another logical move would be the purchase for the RAF of much more capacious and longer-range trans-

of hostile intent? Given the extent of Argentina's losses during the war, and the usual need to replace outdated equipment, such purchases should not be unexpected. The fact that Britain and Argentina have strengthened their forces in the region does not preclude peaceful negotiations, and indeed it is possible that such blatant displays of determination could actually help speed up the negotiating process.

One veteran of the Falklands campaign, the Vulcan, was finally retired as a bomber in December 1982, when the RAF's No 44 Squadron was disbanded. Meanwhile, this service received its 100th Tornado in February 1983. Other air arms are also getting advanced equipment: Pakistan is the latest nation to buy the F-16 Fighting Falcon, the F-18A Hornet is now operational with the US Marine Corps and has been received by the Canadian Armed Forces, and in January 1983 India became the second nation to operate the Sea Harrier. Continued large-scale modern aircraft production in the Soviet Union was highlighted in September 1982 when the Japan Air Self-Defence Force intercepted five Tupolev Tu-22M Backfires near the Sea of Japan. Japanese sources numbered the aircraft among the ninety or so Backfires now based in the Far East, where they supplement a force of SS-20 mobile ballistic missiles. The USAF is to counter these deployments by replacing the conventionally armed Stratofortress bombers based at Guam in the Pacific with SRAM-carrying B-52Gs.

International collaboration in aerospace is nothing new, but some recent partnerships have made news over the past year. Grumman Aerospace is to build the composite wings and vertical tail for the new Israeli Lavi lightweight fighter, and for the first time Britain is collaborating with Saab-Scania of Sweden on a major aircraft project, with British Aerospace assisting in the design and development of the carbon-fibre wings for the JAS 39 Gripen combat aircraft. Saab-Scania has also made aviation history on the commercial front by collaborating with Fairchild Industries on the Saab-Fairchild 340 twin-turboprop airliner. This is the first such agreement between European and US companies. Britain and Romania also had something to celebrate when in September 1982 the first BAe One-Eleven airliner to be assembled in Romania was rolled out as a Rombac 1-11 Series 560. The second 1-11 was to be seen at the Paris Show.

On June 16, 1983, the European Space Agency's Ariane launch vehicle successfully put two satellites into orbit, so proving itself at last to be a realistic rival to the Nasa Shuttle as a commercial payload launcher. Two days later America achieved one of the most keenly awaited Shuttle firsts when Sally Ride became the first US woman in space. Details of this mission, STS-7, are to be found in Reginald Turnill's *Space goes commercial*. STS-7 was also the first ever mission on which five people were launched in one vehicle. MJHT

port aircraft to take over some duties from the overworked Hercules. The argument for a new heavyweight transport for the RAF is discussed by Bill Gunston in this *Review*. A new airfield could also prove to be of immense value in the longer term, accommodating the commercial air traffic certain to result from any economic development of the islands or their waters.

Most people believe that there will eventually be a political solution that will satisfy Britain, Argentina and the islanders themselves. But those who see little prospect of agreement can point to Argentina's continuing rearmament effort. In November 1982 France resumed delivery of Super Etendard naval fighters and Exocet anti-shipping missiles to Argentina, and that December saw the start of deliveries of Mirage IIICJs from Israel. But are these and other acquisitions proof

The contributors

Don Berliner has been a freelance writer for more than fifteen years. He specialises in sporting and historical aviation subjects, is an experienced air racing and aerobatic official, and has supervised FAI record attempts. His most recent publication is a history of absolute world air speed records entitled *Victory Over The Wind*, and other projects include a series of aviation books for young enthusiasts and another on jet aircraft of the Second World War for scale modellers.

Peter J. Bish spent part of his childhood living close to London Heathrow's 10L approach, resulting in a keen interest in aircraft and aviation photography. A particular enthusiasm for lighter-than-air craft took him to many balloon meetings and eventually he achieved an early ambition by making a flight in Cameron O-84 G-AYJZ. Thereafter he helped form the Dante Balloon Group. He gained his PPL to pilot balloons in 1973 and has since logged about 300 flying hours in ten countries. He also holds a fixed-wing licence and has a share in Piper Clipper G-BIAP. Currently employed as an air traffic controller at Heathrow, he also writes articles on aviation subjects and has had nearly 1,400 photographs published.

Steve Broadbent spent nine years at British Aerospace Warton, first as an apprentice and then as a flight test engineer on the Jaguar project, before joining *Flight International* in 1974 as avionics editor. Returning to BAe, he worked on the early stages of the AEW Nimrod programme and as an airliner sales executive. In 1980 he moved to a public relations consultancy, where he handled the account of a high-technology client in the aerospace industry. He turned to freelance writing, specialising in aerospace, early in 1983.

Austin J. Brown runs the Bristol-based Aviation Picture Library, which specialises in aviation photography for publishers, publicity agencies, manufacturers and airlines. He is also a freelance aircraft captain, having been trained on a course sponsored jointly by Cambrian Airways and the British Government, and has since flown aircraft ranging from the DC-3 to the Bandeirante.

Terry Gander spent five years in the RAF, specialising in air radar. After leaving the service he went into the new and expanding technology of computers. Some years later he began writing and now works full-time for Jane's. He has produced more than twenty books on military subjects and has contributed to *Jane's Defence Review* and other publications. He is also a keen aviation photographer.

Bill Gunston served as a flying instructor in the RAF at the end of the Second World War and in 1951 joined the magazine *Flight International*, being appointed Technical Editor in 1955. He became a full-time freelance writer in 1970 and has since been responsible for a prodigious output of books, magazine articles and professional reports.

Mike Hirst is an aeronautical engineer and writer. Formerly Technical Editor of *Flight International*, he currently writes about military aircraft and systems, and is a member of the *Jane's Avionics* team.

Philip Jarrett AMRAeS began writing on aeronautical history in 1967, when he was a library assistant at the Royal Aeronautical Society. He subsequently became assistant editor of the Society's newspaper, *Aerospace*, and in 1973 he joined the newly launched *Aeroplane Monthly* in a similar capacity. Since 1980 he has been production editor of *Flight International*. A member of Cross & Cockade and Air-Britain, he has contributed papers and articles on pioneer aviation and other subjects to a variety of private and commercial publications.

Chris Kjelgaard has been on the air transport staff of *Flight International* for the past 2½ years and has written extensively on every facet of the airline industry. He has contributed to several other magazines and publications, and has frequently broadcast on radio and TV stations in Britain, Europe and North America.

Roy McLeavy was a frequent freelance contributor to the aviation press before launching the magazine *Hovering Craft & Hydrofoil* in 1961. He has been editor and compiler of *Jane's Surface Skimmers* since 1966 and has also written several books on advanced marine concepts, one of which has been published in the USSR. He is currently working on two new books: *Military*

Hovercraft and *Amphibious Operations — Advances in Technology and Tactics.*

Jay Miller is an author and publisher and has been responsible for several books, the latest of which is a definitive work on the General Dynamics F-16 Fighting Falcon. He is currently working on a study of the Lockheed U-2.

David Mondey FRHistS, AMRAeS, formerly an engineer in the RAF, has written or edited more than twenty aviation books. Some of the most recent include *Giants in the Sky* and *Milestones of Flight*, the latter a chronology of aerospace achievements written with Michael Taylor.

Kenneth Munson AMRAeS, ARHistS has contributed to *Jane's All the World's Aircraft* since 1968, working as assistant editor with special responsibility for much of the main aircraft section, sailplanes, microlights, hang-gliders and RPVs. He also has more than forty books to his name.

John W. R. Taylor FRAeS, FRHistS, FSLAET began his aviation career in 1941 as a member of Sir Sydney Camm's wartime fighter design team at Hawker Aircraft Ltd. He became a full-time writer in 1955 and has been editor of *Jane's All the World's Aircraft* for the past 23 years. Well over two hundred other aviation books bearing his name have been pub-

lished, one of them an award-winning history of the RAF Central Flying School.

Michael J. H. Taylor has been a full-time aviation writer for the past 14 years. He began his career by contributing sections to *Jane's All the World's Aircraft*, *Jane's Fighting Ships* and *Jane's Weapon Systems*, and went on to write books for a number of publishers. He compiles the homebuilt aircraft section of *Jane's All the World's Aircraft*, is editor of this *Review*, was editor of and major contributor to the five-volume *Jane's Encyclopedia of Aviation*, and has had more than forty books published. His most recent works include books on the history and development of jet fighters and jet bombers and on current commercial and military aircraft, *Planemakers 1: Boeing, Fantastic Flying Machines*, and, with David Mondey, *Milestones of Flight*. Future publications include a history of Short Brothers in the *Planemakers* series.

Reginald Turnill, internationally known writer and broadcaster, was the BBC's aerospace correspondent from 1958 to 1976. He began his writing and reporting career during the 1930s, covering many of the most important aviation events of the period. The launch of Sputnik 1 in 1957 prompted his specialisation in spaceflight and he is currently editor of and principal contributor to *Jane's Spaceflight Directory*.

Birds don't have bank accounts

John W. R. Taylor

Armed with cruise missiles, and with range greatly extended by flight refuelling, the B-1B offers far greater versatility than any missile.

Most aviation histories begin with the profound remark that men dreamed of flying like the birds for thousands of years. At last, Orville and Wilbur Wright succeeded in becoming airborne in a mechanical bird which, in the disrespectful words of one aviation engineer, "had its backside at the front and no legs". With its front elevator, and skids instead of wheels, the 1903 Wright biplane was hardly a thing of beauty; but it did fly, and pointed the way to better designs. In parallel, its builders pointed the way to what was to become a dominant feature of the whole aviation scene by the then far-off

1980s. They decided in 1905 that it was time to suspend flying and to ensure that their aeroplane would produce a healthy profit to repay their expenditure of six and a half years of patient effort and almost $1,000 in cash on the original biplane alone. So they put away their aeroplane and remained on the ground for nearly three years. Unfortunately for their hopes of becoming flying's first millionaires, this gave European pioneers time to catch up with more practical aeroplanes.

Today, in an age obsessed with finance, the vast potential of aviation is being steadily eroded. Great

11

airlines like British Airways may offer standards of safety and service second to none over routes spanning the globe. But unless they also show large annual profits they are compelled to shed staff, dispose of aircraft and cut their route networks until the finance people are satisfied.

An extreme example of where such policies may lead was given in a 1983 *Washington Post* account of passenger flights on the domestic services of a foreign airline that must remain nameless. At one destination, it reported: "The creaky aeroplane headed into its final approach, 12 hours overdue and shuddering so fiercely that the cockpit door kept swinging ajar, its hinge screws dancing merrily in threadbare holes." The interiors of some aircraft were described as "shabby, with seats loosened from their bolts and meal trays flopping. Light switches seem to be mainly for decoration. A trip to the toilet can end in a wrestling match with an unclosable door . . . . Flights often are cancelled if not enough customers show up. Overbooking, however, poses little practical problem. A European businessman recalled how six (local people) were seated on collapsible canvas stools on a crowded flight last year . . . . 'Seat belts? The chairs didn't even have backs', he said".

Maintenance standards were equally worrying. Airports were described as having few navigation aids, spotty security, and crews lacking in modern training. Fares charged to tourists were three times higher than that nation's citizens were asked to pay. Yet this airline must surely be a paragon to accountants everywhere. It made a profit of nearly £80 million in 1982, and was expected to do even better in 1983.

By comparison, British Airways can claim that it made an operating profit of £190 million in 1982 before deduction of interest charges, compared with £13 million in 1981, after years of heavy losses. But, with debts totalling more than £1,000 million, its balance sheet may appeal more to financial wheelers and dealers than to the British taxpayers, who are likely to settle the £1,000 million overdraft when Mrs Thatcher's government sells British Airways under its privatisation policy.

Private ownership may ease the state's financial burden, but will it continue to give British Airways' passengers the same standards of safe, efficient service? Those who expect annual profits from a planned purchase of shares would do well to study first the everyday costs of running a major international airline, and of buying new aircraft when they are needed. They would not be encouraged by the 1982 results of America's eleven major, privately owned operators. Of the entire group, only US Air, Northwest Orient and United recorded net profits. The eleven airlines suffered a cumulative net loss of $742 million (about £490 million), compared with a $620 million loss in 1981. Total operating loss was $600 million. Pan American,

perhaps the nearest US equivalent to British Airways, recorded its highest ever net loss of $492.5 million (£324 million).

Figures in hundreds of millions are beyond the comprehension of most people. Easier to understand is the fact that it would cost every man, woman and child in the UK about £18 to wipe off British Airways' debts so that its new owners could start with a clean balance sheet. Such a proposal would generate fierce opposition from some quarters; but how much is a good airline worth as a national asset, whoever owns it?

The Concorde has always presented a good case in favour of public support for aviation. It was designed primarily to carry 100 passengers at twice the speed of sound between Europe and the east coast of America. This it has done with a remarkable standard of safety and reliability, making supersonic air transportation routine in the process. It was never designed to make a fortune, and recoup its development cost, during a period when fuel costs would treble without warning. Yet British Airways Concordes are now able to show an operating profit on routes between London, Washington and New York.

Those who criticise Concorde's noise, notably during take-off, forget that aircraft noise was not yet recognised as a social problem at the time of its design. It could have been fitted with new and quieter engines, and could have been made twice as large to ensure high operating profits from the start. In either case, the development cost would have risen to such an extent that the whole Concorde programme would probably have been abandoned before the first flight of a prototype.

Anyone who still feels that the cost of the Concorde programme has been excessive should remember that the United States spent far more money on its own supersonic airliner projects but gave up when the chosen Boeing design became increasingly impractical as it was developed. Russia built thirteen of its Tu-144 "Concordskis" but lost two in accidents and operated the others only briefly before discarding them as unable to achieve their promised performance.

So, only Britain and France have gained the experience and technical competence that stem from the successful development and operation of a fleet of supersonic airliners. Their peoples have only governments and accountants to blame if no second-generation, larger, quieter Super Concorde is produced to reap the immense financial rewards that technological leadership in the production of such an aircraft would offer.

For more than 25 years UK governments, in particular, have allowed themselves to be persuaded by misguided financial and defence "experts" against supporting fully the nation's aerospace industry. Back in 1957 a Defence White Paper implied that the Royal Air Force would need no new fighters and bombers after those that were then being developed. Instead, the

Harrier, the only NATO aircraft that could stay in action after its runways had been cratered. *(BAe)*

exercise of future defensive and strategic air power was to be entrusted to missiles. The Air Staff was convinced that such a concept was stupid, and had the courage to say so. The rightness of its belief is evident in the fact that today the Tornado is entering service in both attack and air-defence versions, and yet another fighter is being developed in prototype form as the Advanced Combat Aircraft (ACA). But governments seldom learn from past mistakes.

For example, the Harrier has shown itself unique and extremely effective in both its RAF and naval Sea Harrier forms. The Falklands campaign of 1982 could not have been fought without it. In any future European war, big or small, it might well be the only first-line combat aircraft able to operate after airfields had been cratered in the first minutes of a confrontation. Yet the British Government has happily passed to McDonnell Douglas of the USA the leadership in developing and manufacturing the second-generation Harrier II, and has not requested V/Stol capability in the ACA. One can only wonder what price the Soviet Union would be willing to pay for Harrier technology and manufacturing expertise, to make possible a V/Stol successor to its Yak-36 Forger.

At no time has the Soviet Union slackened the pace of its development of new combat aircraft, which are viewed correctly as a vital component of its forces despite the possession of immense numbers of nuclear, chemical and conventional missiles of every conceivable type and range. During the past twelve months, the new Sukhoi Su-25 Frogfoot attack aircraft, in the class of the USAF's A-10 Thunderbolt II, has operated in partnership with Mi-24 Hind helicopter gunships against Mujaheddin rebels in Afghanistan. It is easy to suggest that it might not be adequate for deployment to the Central Front in Europe, but that would be true only as long as Nato opposition survived and could be put into the air from vulnerable runways and in Europe's unpredictable weather.

Nor should too much encouragement be derived from the overwhelming success ratio achieved by Israeli fighter pilots in combat with MiG fighters of various kinds over the Bekaa Valley in Lebanon. Thanks to their E-2C Hawkeye Awacs aircraft, the Israelis knew the precise location of every enemy aircraft coming their way, and could plan their interceptions to ensure the maximum likelihood of success. The quality of their F-15 and F-16 fighters, the air-to-air and air-to-surface missiles they used, their ECM and decoys, and their pilots, was uniformly high.

The balance of power might produce quite different results in Europe. Both sides have the benefit of Awacs direction now that the original ineffective Soviet Tu-126 Moss is being replaced by the far superior Mainstay, an Awacs version of the four-turbofan Il-76 transport. Soon the present generation of MiG and Sukhoi fighters will be replaced by the MiG-29 Fulcrum and Su-27 Flanker, in the class of America's F-18 and F-15 respectively, and by the MiG Foxhound successor to the MiG-25 Foxbat.

The number of Su-24 Fencer attack aircraft and Tu-22M Backfire-B bombers facing Nato already totals many hundreds, and prototypes of the new Tupolev strategic bomber known to Nato as Blackjack will soon be followed by the first trickle of production aircraft. Bigger than even the B-52, and nearly 805km/hr (500mph) faster than the B-1B, Blackjack should convince the British Government of its dangerous error in believing that the day of the big bomber is past.

By comparison, the £11,000 million or more that Britain will spend on the Royal Navy's Trident missile submarine force represents a poor investment. There is not the remotest possibility that Trident could ever be launched in anger without precipitating or following the blasting of the UK from the map, which is hardly what one means by defence. Nor will its possession add materially to the huge overkill capability of our allies in the deterrent role. The only genuine hope for the future lies in progressive and early multilateral reduction of missile strength, both strategic and intermediate-range. Meanwhile, two or three squadrons of highly versatile B-1Bs would represent a far better investment for Britain than a fleet of Trident submarines.

It would be pleasing to add that such a purchase of B-1Bs would contribute to a growing standardisation of equipment, and two-way traffic in military procurement, among Nato forces. Unfortunately, Nato standardisation and US willingness to acquire the best of its allies' military wares hardly exist.

Further proof of this came in early 1983, when the US Congress produced a bill excluding British Martin-Baker ejection seats from the US Navy's F/A-18 Hornet and T-45 Hawk training aircraft. It was useless for the Navy to point out that both types had been designed for, and built to date with, Martin-Baker seats; or that it wanted to continue using the British seats which had already saved some 3,000 American lives. With the votes and support of US seat manufacturers in the minds of Congressmen, and faced by an isolationist objection to spending dollars overseas on anything that could be made in the United States, the Navy lost another Battle of Washington.

So, it seems, the holders of pursestrings have an increasing influence on military purchasing in the West, as well as on the commercial aviation scene. There is little need to emphasise the seriousness of this. Mistakes on the commercial side might shut down an airline or a manufacturer; errors of judgement in the military sphere could lead to the annihilation of whole nations. Yet even small nations which have had recent experience of war can still debate whether the financial cost of effective defence is too high.

At the 1983 Paris Show I was asked to discuss with two very knowledgeable Israeli journalists the merits of Israel Aircraft Industries' new Lavi (Young Lion) fighter. This will be a Mach 1.85 single-seater, intended to replace the A-4 Skyhawk and Kfir C2/C7 in the Israeli Air Force at the beginning of the 1990s. But there are problems. To avoid the transfer to Israel of US advanced technology that would be valuable to a third party, the wings and tail surfaces will be made of composite materials by Grumman in America and exported in a finished state. Similarly, the PW1120 turbofan will be built by Pratt & Whitney and delivered in ready-to-fit form. This will inhibit exports of the Lavi, as the USA would refuse to supply these components for aircraft sold to a nation of whose policies it did not entirely approve.

The first question asked by the journalists was whether Israel is wise to spend money on an aircraft with so little potential for earning export profits. This was answered by another question: "Does your air force need the Lavi?" The response was an immediate "Yes, of course it does," leading to the only possible comment: "Then you *have* to build the Lavi, don't you?"

By coincidence, at the Paris Show four years earlier a similar conversation had persuaded a Swedish newspaperman that his nation had to build the JAS 39 Gripen fighter because it would never get precisely what it needed from anywhere else. The Israelis have to accept the added worry that the supply of major components and spares throughout the long life of the Lavi will depend on the continued goodwill of a very unpredictable US Congress.

It is easy to believe, smugly, that Western Europe has done rather better than the USA by working in international partnership on aerospace programmes. But even the most successful teams usually stay together for only one specific programme and then go their separate ways. Aérospatiale and British Aerospace created a team to develop and build Concorde, and then dispersed it. British Aerospace and Dassault/Breguet worked together on the Jaguar while, simultaneously, Dassault continued its efforts to persuade potential Jaguar customers of the superiority of its own fighters, and to offer the Dassault-Breguet/Dornier Alpha Jet as the No 1 competitor to BAe's Hawk. The Franco-British team is unlikely to survive the end of

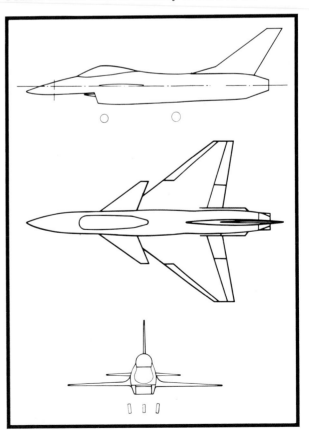

Left: **System training replica of the T-45 Hawk. British ejection seats may have to be replaced by seats of US manufacture.** *(BAe)*

Right: **First official three-view drawing of the IAI Lavi.** *(IAI)*

the Jaguar project, and the same will probably be true of the Franco-German Alpha Jet partnership.

Dassault is already working on its ACX aircraft as the basis for the next French Air Force fighter, while BAe has British Government support for its ACA, and West Germany is reluctant to abandon its own TKF future combat aircraft project. Yet the last thing Europe needs is three different fighters designed to do much the same job.

Only in the Airbus consortium are European partners continuing to work together with obvious enthusiasm on future projects, as the company nibbles ever deeper into what appeared formerly to be Boeing's worldwide monopoly. Even here, though, the British Government is currently restraining its enthusiasm as it weighs the cost of participation in the next-stage A320 programme, which is essential to complete Airbus's selection of intermediate-range passenger airliners. As usual the problem is that participation will cost money, and Boeing might be unkind enough to produce a competitor for the A320 at just the wrong time. It must be difficult, even for people whose lives are bound up with monetarism, to have so little faith in an industry that produced the Concorde, Harrier, Hawk, Jaguar, Nimrod, A300, A310 and a high proportion of the great aeroplanes of history.

In one positive development, however, the British Army is being allowed to evaluate an all-British aeroplane, with the prospect of ordering an initial batch of one hundred. Army pilots have flown two types of

Above: **Among the new generation of Dassault-Breguet combat aircraft is the Mirage 2000N, designed to replace the Mirage IVA as France's nuclear attack aircraft.** *(Brian M. Service)*

Left: **The Baroudeur, one of several French microlights currently under evaluation as ultra-lightweight attack aircraft.** *(Brian M. Service)*

British microlight aircraft to discover if they have any capability that would be of value to the Army. Microlights are fun, but could they survive in any place where the enemy had shoulder-fired surface-to-air missiles? There are plenty of ambitious builders willing to fit rocket launchers and other weapons to their microlights to demonstrate a professed combat potential. Their numbers might diminish rapidly if real proof, over guerrilla territory somewhere, were called for.

The real significance of microlights is that they have brought back something of the airmindedness and amateur enthusiasm that gave flying such a boost in the 1930s. Latest estimates suggest a worldwide total of well over 36,000 aircraft in this under-150kg (330lb) empty weight category, although their safety record cannot be regarded as satisfactory at present. Once again, history provides a parallel. Just 60 years ago, in 1923, the Royal Aero Club of the United Kingdom organised a Light Aeroplane Competition at Lympne in Kent. One prize of £500 was offered for the aircraft able to fly farthest on a single gallon of petrol, using an engine of not more than 750cc capacity. It was won jointly by two motor-gliders which each covered 87½ miles on their one gallon.

The de Havilland company had entered for the competition a single-seat lightplane named the Humming Bird, which was so superior to the motor-gliders in most respects that the Air Ministry ordered 12 for evaluation by the Royal Air Force. With a 750cc engine and top speed of 122km/hr (76mph), they were clearly of no practical use whatsoever but they were great fun to fly. At the Central Flying School FO H.R.D. Waghorn (later to win the 1929 Schneider Trophy contest in a Supermarine S.6 seaplane) flew a Humming Bird through a hangar after noticing that the doors were open at each end.

Capt Geoffrey de Havilland realised that such exploits did not make the Humming Bird the aeroplane that the Air Ministry was seeking as suitable training equipment for civilian flying clubs, which were to receive a government subsidy. So he set to work to design the right aeroplane for the job. The result was the two-seat Moth, initially with a 44.7kW (60hp) Cirrus engine, on which the flying-club movement was founded throughout much of the world.

Today we need a thoroughly modern "Moth" to offer a more practical alternative to microlights. The original DH Moth of 1925 could be bought for £595, flown by almost anybody, towed behind a family car and kept in a garage with its wings folded. The 1983 Paris Show saw the debut of a little aeroplane known simply as the ATL (*avion très léger*, very light aeroplane), which could prove to be its modern counterpart. Designed and built by Pierre Robin, who has already delivered some 2,500 conventional lightplanes from his Dijon factory, it evolved from the French aero clubs' plea for an economical ultralight two-seater that would combine high safety with reasonable performance.

Jacques Buchoux of the JPX company embodied his motorcycle experience in a 1,300cc three-cylinder radial engine only 50cm (20in) in diameter, which gives 35kW (47hp) for modest fuel consumption. Built in only ten months, the prototype fitted snugly into the beautifully streamlined ATL airframe that had been taking shape at Dijon. To keep down weight and cost this had a laminated glassfibre/honeycomb/epoxy fuselage, wooden wings and V tail covered with Dacron fabric, and metal control surfaces. Pierre Robin estimates that production models could be sold for Fr150,000 (£12,600), compared with anything from Fr230,000 (£19,300) to Fr277,000 (£23,250) for a Cessna 152 in France.

The ATL spans 10m (32ft 9½in) and has a take-off weight of 420kg (925lb) with crew of two and 520lit (11 Imp gal) of fuel. This is expected to give a range of

800km (497 miles) at 136km/hr (85mph). Maximum speed is estimated at 180km/hr (112mph), stalling speed a mere 66km/hr (41mph), take-off run 115m (377ft) from a hard runway, and landing run 90m (295ft). If the ATL proves as good as it looks, and the French Government produces the anticipated Fr4 million of state aid needed to get production under way, Robin expects to build about 100 a year for ten years, with 400 going to the French National Aeronautic Federation for use by aero clubs.

Already, therefore, the shape of aviation well into the next century is becoming apparent. One-time fears of imminent fuel exhaustion seem to have been allayed by the discovery of new reserves and the development of more fuel-efficient engines. Beech in America has had great success in running aircraft and land vehicles on liquid methane alternative fuel, and the French are flying several light aircraft on liquid petroleum gas.

The survivability of military aircraft in combat is being enhanced by the application of what was once known as "stealth" technology but has been renamed "low-observability" in the best US tradition of never using a seven-letter word when sixteen letters are available. Forward-swept wings will appear on some fighters, and multi-blade propfans driven by turboprop engines are likely to supersede turbofans on some transport aircraft.

We shall see during the next twelve months the first example of Oleg Antonov's new giant military transport, in the C-5 Galaxy class and giving the Soviet Air Force the tank carrier it needs urgently to replace ageing An-22s. The first small anti-helicopter helicopters cannot be far behind. Add to such programmes the still secret Lockheed F-19 Stealth fighter from the Skunk Works at Burbank, and the low-observability bomber being developed by Northrop to follow the B-1B, and the future is clearly full of interest.

All that is missing is a sense of political urgency to ensure that there will be a future, through meaningful proposals and progress at the East/West arms limitation talks. Up to now the threat and cost of nuclear missiles, held by both sides in ever increasing numbers, have diverted attention from far more vital, non-military aviation tasks such as helping to feed the world's 4,600 million people — a total predicted to increase to 6,300 million by the end of the century. More than half of the developing nations will be unable to feed themselves by then. Even in South America, where no country is currently incapable of feeding itself, people go hungry because the food is not where the people are. Here, surely, is a challenge worthy of aviation.

There are plenty of good agricultural aircraft capable of making unproductive regions fertile, improving poor grazing land by top-dressing, and air-dropping seed for food crops or for trees for the 2,000 million people who will lack essential firewood by the year 2000. Aircraft can restrict by pesticide spraying the ravages of insects and plant diseases, which destroy much of the food that is grown. They can carry huge quantities of food speedily and securely from places that have a wheat surplus or a butter mountain to where people are starving.

Do we really relish the thought that someone might write one day: "What a pleasant place this Earth would have been if those who wanted food had had money to buy it, and those who wanted missiles had had less money and more sense"?

Hughes Helicopters' design to meet the US Army's LHX requirement for an air-to-air combat helicopter. (Hughes)

Chronology

June 3, 1982—June 3, 1983

David Mondey

1982

June 3
An RAF Vulcan operating in support of British forces on the Falkland Islands was intercepted in Brazilian airspace and escorted to Rio de Janeiro by Brazilian Air Force F-5Es.

June 4
The Swedish Parliament approved the JAS 39 Gripen development and initial procurement contracts awarded to the JAS Industry Group on April 30. It is planned to produce 140 examples of this multi-role combat aircraft for service with the Swedish Air Force.

June 6
Ten Mirage 5P fighter-bombers were transferred from Peru to Argentina.

June 6
Backed by extensive air strikes, Israeli armour and infantry invaded southern Lebanon.

June 8
Argentinian aircraft attacked British Task Force ships at Bluff Cove, causing heavy loss of life.

June 12
HMS *Glamorgan* was struck by a land-based Exocet missile fired from Port Stanley. Thirteen of the crew were lost but the destroyer remained operational.

June 14
Fokker handed over to the Royal Netherlands Air Force the 100th F-16 Fighting Falcon assembled by the company. Of this total, 38 had been delivered to the Royal Norwegian Air Force.

June 14
First flight of a homebuilt example of the Italian Falco F.8L two-seat lightplane. The aircraft was built by Larry Wohlers and the flight took place at Tucson, Arizona.

June 14
Argentinian forces in the Falkland Islands surrendered. Including captured machines, known Argentinian aircraft losses totalled 109 but may actually have been as high as 130.

June 14
Beech Aircraft began flight tests of a then unidentified pressurised aircraft with a single turboprop engine. Since named the Model 38P Lightning, it has a fuselage and wing basically similar to those of the Model 58P Baron.

June 19
First flight of the second Lear Fan 2100 prototype. This aircraft differs from the first in having a fuselage lengthened by 0.305m (1ft) and a modified engine installation and cooling system.

June 21
Westland Helicopters announced that it had started development of an anti-armour helicopter designated Lynx 3. It is intended to carry a wide range of anti-tank missile systems.

Mock-up of the Westland Lynx 3, with a mast-mounted sight and provision for Hellfire missiles (June 21, 1982). *(Westland)*

June 22

First flight of the British Aerospace VC10 K2 flight-refuelling tanker for the RAF.

June 22

The first CFM56-2-engined Boeing KC-135R Stratotanker was rolled out at Wichita, Kansas. Subject to satisfactory flight tests, some 300 Stratotankers will receive the new engine.

June 29

Lockheed-Georgia completed ahead of schedule the conversion of 270 US Air Force C-141A StarLifter transports to stretched C-141B standard. Flight-refuelling capability was also incorporated.

July 1

Denmark's three armed services were integrated. Strength of the Air Force is set at 129 aircraft, including 92 fighters, by the end of 1984.

July 1

UK Defence Secretary John Nott announced that 14 British Aerospace Sea Harriers were to be ordered to cover attrition in the Falklands War and to increase the Royal Navy's total holding.

July 2

The US Air Force announced that the Fairchild Republic submission had been selected to meet its New Generation Trainer requirement. An initial contract covers design finalisation, development, manufacture and test of two NGT prototypes and two static airframes.

July 2

Tom Jewett, president of Quickie Aircraft Corporation, died when *Free Enterprise*, designed for a non-stop round-the-world flight, crashed at Mojave, California.

July 2

The Federal German Navy received the first four of a planned total of 112 Panavia Tornadoes.

July 3

First flight of the first of two General Dynamics F-16XL prototypes. This aircraft is the single-seat model of an advanced version of the F-16 Fighting Falcon, which features a new, highly swept cranked-arrow wing with a total area of more than double that of the standard F-16 wing.

July 10

First flight of the General Dynamics Advanced Fighter Technology Integration (AFTI) F-16. Embodying lessons from the company's earlier control-configured vehicle (CCV) programmes, the AFTI aircraft is being used to demonstrate new air-combat techniques.

July 14

First flight, at Harbin, of the Chinese turboprop-powered Y11T light transport prototype. This is a development of the piston-engined Y11, incorporating a stretched fuselage to seat up to 17 passengers in a commuter configuration.

July 16

Hamble Airfield Properties, a consortium formed by a number of businessmen, acquired from British Airways the College of Air Training at Hamble, Hampshire. It was intended that it should continue to train civil pilots.

July 23

The US Deputy Secretary of State announced that America was prepared to sell advanced military equipment to India.

July 23

Japan initiated a £35 billion five-year defence programme that includes the supply of more than 500 new aircraft for the JASDF, JGSDF and JMSDF.

July 23

The Spanish Government announced that it would procure 84 McDonnell Douglas F-18 Hornets to replace F-4s and F-5s currently in Air Force service.

July 25

Equipped with new Mitsubishi T-2 supersonic jet trainers, the JASDF's Blue Impulse aerobatic display team gave its first public demonstration, at Matsushima Air Base.

July 24

Of the four British Aerospace Hawks acquired by the Zimbabwe Air Force during June, one was destroyed and three seriously damaged by sabotage at Thornhill AFB. A number of other aircraft were destroyed or damaged in the attack.

July 27

The 100th anniversary of the birth of Sir Geoffrey de Havilland was marked by the Royal Aeronautical Society with a photographic exhibition covering his life and work.

July 28

McDonnell Douglas rolled out at St Louis, Missouri, the first CF-18 Hornet for the Canadian Armed Forces.

July 28

A new Douglas DC-3 conversion, developed by the United States Aircraft Corporation and powered by two Pratt & Whitney Aircraft of Canada PT6A-45R turboprops, was flown for the first time. Scene of the flight was Van Nuys, California.

July 29

Mexico's leading airline, Mexicana (Compania Mexicana de Aviacion), was nationalised.

July 29
First flight of the Mike Smith XP-99 Prop-Jet, a turboprop-powered six-seat cabin monoplane.

July 30
FAA certification of the Boeing Model 767-200 wide-body medium-range commercial transport, powered initially by Pratt & Whitney JT9D-7R4D turbofans.

August 1
First flight of the British Aerospace 146-200 four-turbofan short-range transport aircraft.

August 4
First flight of the first CFM56-2 turbofan-engined Boeing KC-135R flight-refuelling tanker.

August 5
An Airbus A310, the first to be powered by General Electric CF6-80A turbofans, made its first flight, taking off from and landing at Toulouse.

August 11
The first McDonnell Douglas KC-10A Extender, a flight-refuelling tanker version of the company's DC-10 wide-body transport, was delivered to the US Air Force's 9th Air Refuelling Squadron at March AFB, California.

August 19
The first production Shorts 360 made its first flight, at Belfast, Northern Ireland, before being flown to Farnborough, Hampshire, to take part in the SBAC Show.

August 19
The first Boeing 767-200 for airline service was delivered to United Airlines. This operator began revenue services with the type on September 8.

August 19
In California the Hawk GafHawk 125 Stol turboprop-powered light freighter prototype was flown for the first time.

August 23
The first three of seven Aérospatiale SA.330L Pumas assembled by Nurtanio at Bandung were handed over to the Air Force of the Indonesian Armed Services.

August 30
First flight of the Northrop F-5G (now F-20) Tigershark export fighter prototype, from Edwards AFB.

September 1
The first Helwan-assembled Dassault-Breguet/Dornier Alpha Jet for the Egyptian Air Force made its first flight. A total of 45 have been ordered for the EAF.

September 1
A second squadron of Boeing Vertol Chinooks, No 7 Squadron, was formed by the Royal Air Force at Odiham, Hampshire.

September 3
First flight of the Beechcraft 1900 Airliner transport, at Wichita, Kansas.

September 5
The UK Secretary of State for Industry announced that Westland Helicopters Ltd had been granted £41 million in launch aid for the -200 and -300 versions of the Westland 30.

Boeing 767-200 delivered to Delta Air Lines on October 25, 1982, and put into service on December 15. *(Boeing)*

September 5

General Electric began flight tests of the CT7 turbo-prop engine in the port nacelle of a Grumman Gulfstream I. The CT7 has been selected to power the new Saab-Fairchild 340 transport.

September 8

Dornier gained certification of the 228-200 lengthened-fuselage version of its new commuter/utility transport aircraft.

September 10

First flight of the Mudry CAP X two-seat, lightweight, low-cost basic trainer.

September 14

Japan Air Self-Defence Force F-4EJ Phantoms intercepted five Soviet Tupolev Tu-22M Backfire maritime reconnaissance aircraft over the Sea of Japan. Japanese sources estimate that the Soviet Union is basing some 90 of these variable-geometry bomber/maritime reconnaissance aircraft in the Far East.

September 17

First flight of the first production Canadair Challenger 601. This intercontinental-range business/commuter transport has General Electric CF34-1A turbofans and wingtip winglets.

September 18

The first of three Rombac 1-11 Series 560s assembled by Romania's Intreprinderea de Avioane Bucuresti made its first flight. This company is prime contractor for licence production of the British Aerospace One-Eleven.

September 20

First flight of the first prototype of the Hindustan Aeronautics Ajeet Trainer.

September 28

McDonnell Douglas announced receipt of a $15.6 million contract covering further development work on the VTX/TS trainer, based on the British Aerospace Hawk.

September 30

Beirut Airport was reopened to international traffic.

September 30

Landing at Dallas, Texas, H. Ross Perot Jr and J. W. Coburn completed the first round-the-world flight in a helicopter. Starting on September 1, their Bell 206L LongRanger II, *The Spirit of Texas*, completed the 29-stage flight at an FAI-accredited average speed of 56.97km/hr (35.40mph).

Below: **H. Ross Perot Jr inspects equipment at Andrews Air Force Base after completion of the round-the-world flight. Note the 151 US gal auxiliary fuel tank, which increased the LongRanger's range to 1,207km (750 miles) (September 30, 1982).**

Bottom: **Official opening of the extended runway at Manchester International Airport, with a suitably long cake (October 7, 1982).** (*Manchester International Airport/Paul Francis*)

Above: *The Spirit of Texas,* **photographed while making a difficult refuelling stop on board SS** *President McKinley* **in the North Pacific during its round-the-world flight (September 30, 1982).**

Above left: **Jay W. Coburn supervises refuelling during a landing at Laoag in the Philippines (September 30, 1982).**

Left: **The first Romanian-assembled Rombac 1-11 Series 560, photographed in August 1982 before its first flight (September 18, 1982).** (*BAe*)

October 5
First flight tests of the Boeing 747-300, known initially as the Stretched Upper Deck variant of the Model 747. In a standard economy-class configuration this modification provides seats for 69 passengers on the upper deck.

October 7
Official opening of the extended main runway at Manchester International Airport, Lancashire, which now has a length of 3,050m (10,000ft).

October 13

The first of 40 General Dynamics F-16s (32 F-16As and eight F-16Bs) for the Pakistani Air Force was handed over at Fort Worth, Texas.

October 15

Northrop delivered to the Mexican Air Force the 1,000th production example of the F-5E/-5F Tiger II. T-38/F-5 production now exceeds 3,500 aircraft.

October 17

Following completion of the lengthened and strengthened runway at Port Stanley, Falkland Islands, the first of No 29 Squadron's McDonnell Douglas F-4 Phantoms landed there after a ferry flight from Ascension Island.

October 19

British Airways reported a deficit of £544 million on the year's operations. Much of this was attributed to the impending privatisation of the state airline.

October 22

First flight of the Hughes 530E helicopter, which is optimised for operation from hot or high locations.

October 25

British Midland Airways inaugurated its London Heathrow-Glasgow route, on which BMA competes against the British Airways Shuttle.

October 28

Tenth anniversary of the first flight of the Airbus A300. At this point 192 examples had been delivered.

October 29

To reduce losses on Concorde operations Air France terminated its service to Washington. The airline now uses Concordes only on its New York route.

November 1

Two Bell 214ST transport helicopters entered service with British Caledonian Helicopters for use in support of offshore gas/oil rigs and platforms. B.Cal has one more 214ST on order and options on additional aircraft.

November 4

Pan American inaugurated what is claimed to be the world's longest non-stop commercial service. The 12,049km (7,487 miles) sector between Los Angeles and Sydney is flown by the airline's Boeing 747SPs.

November 8

A Tornado of the RAF's No 9 Squadron, based at Honington, made a non-stop out-and-return flight between the UK and Cyprus. The aircraft was refuelled in flight by Victor tankers and a Buccaneer fitted with a buddy refuelling pack.

November 10

First flight of the first production example of the

Dassault-Breguet Mirage F.1CR reconnaissance aircraft.

November 11

Suburban Airlines of Reading, Pennsylvania, accepted its first Shorts 360.

November 18

France resumed deliveries of Dassault-Breguet Super Etendard carrier-based strike fighters and AM.39 Exocet missiles to the Argentinian Navy.

November 20

First flight of the first production Dassault-Breguet Mirage 2000 interceptor/air-superiority fighter.

November 22

British Aerospace announced an agreement with Saab-Scania covering collaboration on design and development of the carbon-fibre wing for the Swedish JAS 39 Gripen multi-role combat aircraft. British Aerospace will build prototype wings, while production examples will be made by Saab-Scania.

December 5

First flight of the Slingsby T67M Firefly, an aerobatic military basic trainer developed from the Fournier RF-6B and Slingsby T67A. It differs from these earlier aircraft in being built mainly of glass-reinforced plastic rather than wood, and has a 119kW (160hp) Avco Lycoming engine.

December 7

The United States Air Force accepted the first five of an initial batch of 11 Sikorsky UH-60A Black Hawk assault helicopters.

December 9

First flight of the Cessna Caravan, a 14-passenger turboprop-powered utility transport.

December 13

British Aerospace 146-100 G-SCHH completed a 51-day tour of Asia, Australia, New Zealand and the Far East. In the course of the tour the aircraft flew some 96,560km (60,000 miles), carried 3,300 passengers on demonstration flights, and suffered only a single, 30min, maintenance delay.

December 15

Contactair of Stuttgart became the first operator to take delivery of a BAe Jetstream 31 commuter/executive transport.

December 15

The Northrop RF-5E Tigereye reconnaissance version of the F-5E Tiger II made its first flight, at Palmdale, California.

December 15

Peru and Dassault signed two contracts covering orders for and options on a total of 22 single-seat and four two-seat Mirage 2000s.

December 16

The Boeing AGM-86B Air-Launched Cruise Missile attained initial operational capability.

December 17

The Rombac 1-11 Series 560 was certificated in Romania. The first delivery to Romanian state airline Tarom was made a week later.

December 18

Argentina received the first of a batch of 22 Mirage IIICJs from Israel. A total of 24 A-4E/A-4H Skyhawks were also due to be delivered from the same source.

December 21

The Dassault-Breguet Mirage IIING (Nouvelle Génération) export fighter prototype, distinguished by foreplanes and a fly-by-wire control system, made its first flight, at Istres.

December 21

The RAF's V-bomber force became aviation history when the last Vulcan bomber unit, No 44 Squadron, was disbanded. Originally planned for early in 1982, the disbandment had been deferred when Argentinian forces invaded the Falkland Islands.

December 21

The Boeing 757 twin-turbofan transport, which has the same fuselage cross-section as the company's 707/727/737 family, gained FAA certification. British CAA certification was gained on January 14, 1983.

December 21

It was stated that the 202nd Squadron, 5th Air Wing, of the Japan Air Self-Defence Force had received a total of 20 F-15J/-15DJ Eagles.

December 23

The UK Secretary of State for Defence announced that two British Aerospace 146-100s would be acquired for use by the RAF as general transports for a two-year period. During that time they would also be evaluated as possible replacements for the Andovers of the Queen's Flight.

December 23

The Shorts Sherpa, a civil freighter variant of the Shorts 330, made its first flight, at Belfast, Northern Ireland. It incorporates a full-width rear-loading door.

December 30

Peregrine Air Services of Aberdeen, Scotland, became the first operator in the UK to take delivery of a British Aerospace Jetstream 31.

December 31

The US Air Force awarded Lockheed an initial $609 million contract to begin production of the Lockheed C-5B Galaxy military transport.

1983
January 7

US Marine Corps fighter squadron VMFA-314 became the first Marine unit to become operational on the McDonnell Douglas F-18A Hornet.

January 14

The six-seat Gulfstream Commander Model 1500 business transport, based on the Gulfstream Aerospace (formerly Gulfstream American) Peregrine military trainer, made its first flight, at Bethany, Oklahoma.

January 17
A new US regional operator, Atlantic Express of Farmingdale, New York, inaugurated scheduled passenger services.

January 21
The first of two Boeing Vertol 234 commercial helicopters for use by Norway's Helikopter Service AS was flown for the first time. These aircraft have the same capacity and North Sea offshore support role as those operated by British Airways Helicopters.

January 25
First flight of the Saab-Fairchild 340 transport. The flight took place exactly in accordance with a schedule planned two years earlier.

January 26
The first of two Westland Sea King Mk 50A helicopters to supplement those already in service was handed over to the Royal Australian Navy.

Below: **Boeing Vertol 234 commercial helicopter operated by Helikopter Service AS (January 21, 1983).**

January 26
The German Air Force took delivery of the last of 175 Dassault-Breguet/Dornier Alpha Jets at Oberpfaffenhofen.

January 27
The first six of 40 General Dynamics F-16 Fighting Falcons were handed over to the Pakistani Air Force.

January 27
The first Sea Harrier FRS51 for the Indian Navy was handed over by British Aerospace at the company's Dunsfold, Surrey, airfield.

January 28
The US National Guard Bureau announced the receipt of its first Sikorsky UH-60 Black Hawk helicopter. The aircraft is serving with an Army National Guard unit, the 1155th Transport Aircraft Maintenance Company.

January 31
Garuda Indonesian Airways took delivery of the first of 20 Fokker F.28 Fellowship Mk 4000s.

January 31
McDonnell Douglas announced that it was to go ahead with development of the DC-9 Super 83. This is an extended-range variant of the DC-9 Super 80, with fuel-efficient Pratt & Whitney JT8D-219 turbofan engines and increased fuel capacity.

February 3
First flight of the Dassault-Breguet Mirage 2000N, a two-seat variant of the Mirage 2000 interceptor/air superiority fighter which will serve with the French Air Force in the all-weather nuclear attack role.

February 8
The first two of eight Grumman E-2C Hawkeye AEW aircraft for the Japan Maritime Self-Defence Force were received at Misawa Air Base.

February 9

First flight, at Marietta, Georgia, of the first rewinged Lockheed C-5A Galaxy. It was redelivered to the US Air Force on February 28.

February 9

British Airways made its first use of the Boeing 757 short/medium-range transport, operating the type on the Shuttle service between London Heathrow and Belfast.

February 10

Airspur Helicopters began services with three of the six Westland 30 helicopters which it had ordered.

February 17

A successful ejection by the pilot of an Italian Air Force F-104S Starfighter brought the number of lives saved by Martin-Baker ejection seats to a total of 5,000.

February 17

Full CAA certification was attained of the British Aerospace 146 short-range transport.

February 17

The Royal Air Force took delivery of its 100th Panavia Tornado multi-purpose combat aircraft.

February 17

It was announced that a joint proposal for the design and development of a JVX (Joint Services Vertical Lift Aircraft) had been submitted by Bell and Boeing Vertol. It is believed that the design is based largely on Bell's Model 301 (XV-15) tilt-rotor research aircraft.

February 23

First flight of the Piper Cheyenne IV, at Lakeland, Florida. Based on the Cheyenne III airframe, it has Garrett TPE333-14 turboprop engines, each developing 746kW (1,000shp).

February 24

A British Aerospace 146-100 returned to the UK following an 18-day tour of Africa. During the tour the

aircraft operated into and out of a number of short airfields which had hitherto normally been used only by turboprops or piston-engined aircraft.

February 25

First flight of the Boeing 707 testbed with a CFM International CFM56-3 turbofan installed in the port inboard position. Test results are contributing to development of the Boeing Model 737-300, which is scheduled to fly in March 1984.

February 25

The last of 182 EMB.326GB Xavantes built under licence by Embraer in Brazil was delivered to the Brazilian Air Force. Deliveries comprised 166 for the Brazilian Air Force, 10 for Paraguay and six for Togo.

February 25

The Challenger 601 long-range business jet received Canadian certification, followed by FAA certification on March 11, 1983.

February 27

The UK Minister for Overseas Development announced plans to build a new airport capable of handling large civil or military transport aircraft on the Falkland Islands.

February 28

First flight of the first production Sikorsky SH-60B Seahawk ASW and anti-ship surveillance and targeting (ASST) helicopter for the US Navy. The aircraft was delivered to the USN on March 24.

March 2

Marconi Avionics announced the receipt of a £30 million contract from General Dynamics for production of a new wide-angle HUD system for the F-16C and F-16D fighters.

March 3

It was announced that Gulfstream Aerospace had ordered 200 units of the Rolls-Royce Tay advanced-technology turbofan, based on the proven core of the RB.183 Spey, to power its Gulfstream IV business jet. The first engines will be delivered in 1986.

March 8

Flight tests of the Pratt & Whitney PW2037 turbofan began, with the new engine fitted to a Boeing 747 in place of one of the standard units.

March 10

L. M. Ericsson of Sweden and Britain's Ferranti signed a contract covering the development and production of radar equipment for the JAS 39 Gripen multi-role combat aircraft.

March 11

A new UK airline, Birmingham Executive Airways, ordered two British Aerospace Jetstream 31s for delivery during 1983.

Right: **Birmingham Executive Airways' first Jetstream 31 (March 11, 1983).** (*BAe*)

March 11

Finnair took delivery of the first of three McDonnell Douglas DC-9 Super 80s, naming it after former Douglas president John C. Brizendine.

March 11

The Airbus A310 gained full French and German certification, covering both the Pratt & Whitney JT9D-7R4 and General Electric CF6-80A powerplants.

March 11

A collaborative agreement covering the development of a new commercial turbofan engine was signed by Fiat, Japanese Aero Engines Corporation, MTU, Pratt & Whitney and Rolls-Royce.

March 11

A new 4,645m² (50,000ft²) final assembly facility for the British Aerospace Jetstream 31 was opened at Prestwick by the Secretary of State for Scotland.

March 16

The German-owned Lockheed F-104G/TF-104G Starfighters operated by the USAF's 69th Tactical Fighter Squadron for the training of German Air Force pilots were withdrawn from service after some 18 years of use.

March 17

British Aerospace announced that Brazilian regional airline Transportes Aereos da Bacia Amazonica (TABA) had ordered two BAe 146-100s for delivery in late 1983.

March 21

The UK Ministry of Defence announced an order for four British Aerospace 125 Series 700 business jets. Destined for service with No 32 Squadron, RAF, they will be used for government and VIP communications.

March 22

British inclusive-tour and charter operator Monarch Airlines took delivery of the first of three Boeing Model 757s, carrying out its inaugural service with the type on March 28.

March 23

Flight tests with Rockwell International's No 2 B-1A prototype resumed at Edwards AFB. It has been modified to take part in the development of the B-1B long-range multi-role strategic bomber.

March 25

Flight testing of the Pratt & Whitney PW1128 fighter engine began, with the powerplant mounted in the starboard position on a Nasa-operated F-15A Eagle. This engine is competing with General Electric's F101DFE (Derivative Fighter Engine) to meet a US Air Force requirement for a new-generation fighter engine.

March 27

The Boeing 747-300 entered service on Swissair's North Atlantic routes.

March 30

Westland Helicopters announced that the UK Ministry of Defence would provide a major share of the funding for the full development of the Sea King composite rotor blades designed and developed by the company.

April 9

World-renowned pioneering pilot Wg Cdr R. H. McIntosh DFC, AFC, RAF (Retd) died at the age of 88. "All-weather Mac" started his career as a civil aircraft captain with Handley Page Transport. His service as a military pilot began in the RFC, and his flying life eventually spanned 54 years from 1917 until his retirement in 1971.

April 9

First flight of the first of two Piper PA-48 Enforcer prototypes. The Enforcer is a turboprop-powered attack aircraft based on the airframe of the North American P-51 Mustang.

April 12

The Bomber Command Museum, a section of the RAF Museum at Hendon, North London, was opened by the Queen Mother.

April 14

The first of five Dassault-Breguet Gardian maritime suveillance aircraft was handed over to the French Navy.

April 18

30th anniversary of the entry into service of the Rolls-Royce Dart turboprop, of which more than 7,100 have been sold. Rated originally at 746kW (1,000shp), this engine has been developed to give an output of up to 2,420ekW (3,245eshp) for a 20 per cent reduction in specific fuel consumption.

April 19

The de Havilland Canada DHC-8 Dash 8 quiet short-range transport was rolled out at Downsview, Ontario.

April 21
Swissair introduced the Airbus A310 on its Zurich-London Heathrow route.

April 24
Air Europe became the third UK airline to inaugurate revenue services with the Boeing 757.

April 25
First flight of Dornier's Do 24TT *Technologieträger* (technology testbed) amphibian. It combines a modernised Dornier Do 24 hull, a new-technology wing of the type developed for the Dornier 228, and three Pratt & Whitney Aircraft of Canada PT6A-45 turboprops.

Above left: **Swissair Boeing 747-300 (March 27, 1983).** (*Boeing*)

Below: **Dornier's Do 24TT amphibian (April 25, 1983).**

Below right: **Roll-out of the BAe 125 Series 800 (May 26, 1983).** (*BAe*)

April 26
Henry Kremer, renowned for his cash prizes to promote the development of man-powered aircraft, made a new award of £100,000 to the Royal Aeronautical Society. It is to be used to promote the development of man-powered aircraft capable of higher airspeed. An initial first prize of £20,000 is offered for completion of a 1.6km (1 mile) circuit in less than three minutes. Subsequent prizes of £5,000 will be given for improvements on the time set by the first winner.

April 26
Airship Industries' second Skyship 500 non-rigid airship made its first flight, at Toronto International Airport.

May 9
Westland Helicopters gained a UK 1983 Design Council Award for the Westland 30 transport helicopter.

May 22
A Robinson R22 lightweight helicopter won the championships of the Helicopter Club of Great Britain.

May 23
The first production British Aerospace 146-100 for service with UK operator Dan-Air was handed over. It was then flown at low altitude over London to emphasise how little noise it generates, before landing at Dan-Air's London Gatwick base.

May 24
Ferranti Computer Systems announced that it had delivered to the RAF an advanced radar data-processing and display system for use in air defence and air traffic control.

May 26
First flight of the British Aerospace 125 Series 800. This latest version of the well established 125 has Garrett TFE731-5 turbofan engines and incorporates many improvements, including a redesigned, new-technology wing of increased span, a new flight deck and a restyled and more spacious cabin.

May 30
British Aerospace Dynamics was contracted by Saab-Scania to design and develop the environmental control system for the JAS 39 Gripen multi-role combat aircraft.

June 1
McAlpine Aviation ordered two BAe Jetstream 31s. To be delivered "green," they will be equipped by McAlpine with a multi-role interior capable of quick changes to 8/9-seat corporate, 12/14-seat executive shuttle, air ambulance or freighter configurations.

June 3
British Aerospace announced receipt of an order from the Mali Government for a BAe 146-100, to be delivered during 1983.

Frogfoot, Fulcrum and Blackjack

Bill Gunston

Northrop A-9A during flight trials against the A-10A. The new Soviet Frogfoot is similar in configuration to this aircraft.

Since the great Aviation Day extravaganza at Domodyedovo Airport, Moscow, on July 9, 1967, the Soviet military aircraft design teams have probably studied several hundred proposals and doubtless built some dozens of prototypes and research aircraft. There has been no public aviation display, however, so we in the West know little of what has been achieved, beyond a few blurred pictures of types that have actually gone into full-scale development and, in two cases, into production. Three are now sufficiently well known to permit a simple assessment.

Frogfoot is the Nato name for a close-support aircraft first identified in 1978 and originally called Ram-J (because it was first seen at the experimental test base at Ramenskoye). Since 1981 it has been openly referred to by the US Department of Defence (DoD) as the Su-25, and this designation is now official. The Sukhoi OKB (experimental aircraft bureau) already had enough on its hands with the Su-22 and Su-24 swing-wing attack families, however, and is also said to have developed yet another new combat aircraft at first dubbed Ram-L and now known as the Su-27 (Nato code name Flanker). Nothing about Frogfoot suggests Sukhoi ancestry, though several features could have originated from the Yakovlev team.

This aircraft is in no sense a fighter, rather a bomber and ground-attack aircraft. For this reason one might have expected it to have an even-number designation, such as Su-26, because odd numbers are reserved strictly for fighters (the Tu-28P and Yak-28P were interceptor [letter P] versions of existing aircraft designed for other purposes, hence the even number). There is no evidence to indicate that this comparatively slow attack aircraft is a close-support version of an aircraft originally designed as a fighter.

For the first 4½ years Washington-derived reports said little about Frogfoot other than that its two jet engines were mounted in pods above the wing. In fact they are nestled under the wing roots, and in layout the aircraft strongly resembles the Northrop A-9A which lost out in competition against the Fairchild Republic A-10A in 1973. Fairchild hung their two engines high on the rear fuselage partly in order to minimise their infra-red (IR) signature and vulnerability to ground fire. But the Soviet designers have judged that these

Artist's impression of two Frogfoot close-support aircraft carrying rocket launchers and other stores.
(US Department of Defence)

considerations are outweighed by the simplicity and easier ground servicing of engines mounted close to the ground. The engines are estimated as having a thrust of 25-40kN (5,620-8,990lb), which is well below the power of the A-10A engines. On the other hand, the Soviet aircraft is smaller than its US counterpart — maximum weight is estimated at about 16,000kg (35,270lb) compared with 22,700kg (50,000lb) — and general speed and agility are said to be superior to those of the A-10A.

Frogfoot has an almost unswept long-span wing giving very good lift at low speeds and with plenty of room for ten pylons plus small tip pods which may well house ECM jammers. A wealth of attack weapons exists for this aircraft, and it has been repeatedly stated that, like its US counterpart, it is built around a powerful gun for use against armour. The long nose looks reminiscent of the Lockheed TR-1 and, as in that machine, has a canopy flush with the top of the fuselage downstream. This is the case with many Soviet tactical aircraft and is

surprising because it gives a poor view except in the forward hemisphere. Certainly Frogfoot can be expected to be well armoured, and its widely spaced jetpipes must expel low-temperature turbofan air from specially cooled shrouds to prevent IR-homing missiles from locking on. It appears to be a single-seater.

Frogfoot has seen extensive action in Afghanistan. It has been used in conjunction with Mi-24 (Hind) gunship helicopters, enabling the best partnership between fixed-wing and helicopter attack aircraft to be worked out in actual operations.

Fulcrum is in a totally different class. This impressive air combat fighter has for four years been described as the MiG-29, and it has also received the code designation Ram-L from its 1979 appearance at Ramenskoye. Early artist's impressions and three-view drawings published in the West have been based more on the F/A-18A Hornet than on the new MiG, but they do at least show the basic features of this aircraft, which faintly resembles a scaled-down MiG-25. It is said to have two relatively small engines (for a Soviet fighter) in the under 10,000kg (22,000lb) thrust class, estimates varying from 6,000kg to 9,000kg with full augmentation. Some observers have speculated that the engines might be the same R-11 or R-13 used in MiG-21s, but

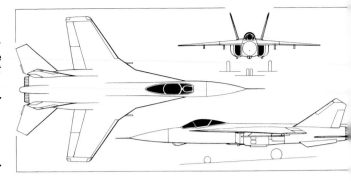

Right: **Three-view of the new Mikoyan MiG-29 Fulcrum fighter.**

Far right: **Comparison chart of some current and future Soviet and US long-range bombers.** (*US Department of Defence*)

Below right: **Artist's impression of Blackjack, probably the most formidable bomber in the world and due for service from the mid-1980s.** (*US Department of Defence*)

this long established engine is very unlikely to have been selected for so new an aircraft. There seems to be little basis for the universal belief that there are in fact two engines.

One of the few bits of actual evidence concerning this fighter is a ciné film showing it demonstrating its manoeuvring capability. Western defence analysts who have seen this agree that, so far as they can tell, the MiG-29 (if that is indeed its true VVS designation) can outmanoeuvre all Western fighters, including the F-16. This is interesting, because quotes from "Washington sources" give the instantaneous turn rate as 16.8°/sec and sustained turn rate as 8.26°/sec, both far short of what can be achieved by a regular F-16. It has become routine to discredit and undervalue Soviet military hardware, perhaps in order to sustain a shaky belief in Western technical superiority. All manner of supposed deficiencies and inadequacies are bandied about as if they are fact. Years later, when knowledge replaces fiction, the derogatory assessments are quietly forgotten. Suffice to say, it is nonsense to imagine that the MiG OKB, of all people, would fail to produce an air combat aircraft superior to all known Western types in flight performance and dogfight agility.

It would also be at least the equal of Western contemporaries in weapons, protection against battle damage and electronic warfare capability. Where it is likely to be inferior is in the technology of the electronics and the engine(s), in which Soviet designers do not appear to be on a par with their Western counterparts. It would not be surprising if, attempting to catch up, they had virtually copied the neat air-cooled APG-66 radar of the original F-16A for Fulcrum. The one extra set of circuits it would need would be a continuous-wave illuminator for guiding semi-active radar-homing (SARH) missiles of the kind used in combination with IR heat-homing missiles on all Soviet fighters. This is a definite advantage over Western fighters, which have a choice between the IR Sidewinder for short ranges and the SARH Sparrow or Sky Flash for longer ranges, but only the one form of guidance for either.

In late 1981 the US magazine *Aviation Week and Space Technology* published what appeared to be a digitally transmitted satellite photograph of a very

34

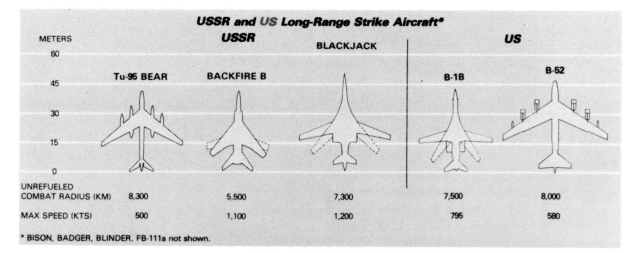

USSR and US Long-Range Strike Aircraft*

	Tu-95 BEAR	BACKFIRE B	BLACKJACK	B-1B	B-52
USSR				**US**	
UNREFUELED COMBAT RADIUS (KM)	8,300	5,500	7,300	7,500	8,000
MAX SPEED (KTS)	500	1,100	1,200	795	580

* BISON, BADGER, BLINDER, FB-111a not shown.

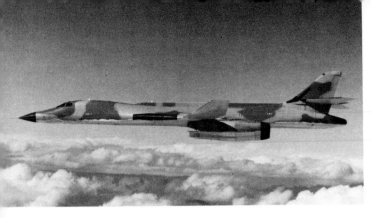

large new Soviet bomber parked at Ramenskoye near two Tu-144 SSTs. The reconstruction appeared distorted by haze, the great distance and by inevitable errors in each frame (these tend to cancel out over a number of frames), but the picture was clear enough to show that the aircraft was a swing-wing bomber remarkably similar to the US B-1 in general configuration, but in fact somewhat larger.

Since 1981 nothing further about this aircraft has appeared, beyond numerous Western three-views,

---

Above: **Rockwell International B-1, forerunner of the B-1B for the USAF.** (*Rockwell*)

Below: **With wings spread and carrying a Kitchen air-to-surface missile under its fuselage, this Backfire-B bomber is evidence of the Soviet lead in advanced bomber deployment.**

artist's impressions and assessments, including the statement (attributed to the CIA by a US senator) that the Soviet Union "will deploy between 50 and 75" of these aircraft by 1990. Initially dubbed Ram-P, this bomber was later given the Nato Air Standards Co-ordinating Committee reporting name of Blackjack.

Blackjack is a "clean sheet of paper" design and so — unlike Backfire — has a completely variable-geometry wing with only a small-span glove (though its colossal chord takes the root forward almost to the cockpit).

There is no doubt whatsoever that it is a bomber, and an aircraft of intercontinental range with heavy weapon loads. It would be reasonable to assume that propulsion might be provided by four engines similar to those of the Tu-144D civil SST. These are from the Koliesov design bureau and are believed to be single-shaft turbojets rated with maximum augmentation at more than 20,000kg (44,090lb) static thrust. This would fit in well with the size of the new bomber, and with a maximum take-off weight in the 250,000kg (550,000lb) class. These figures compare with 13,600kg (30,000lb) thrust and 216,360kg (477,000lb) for the B-1B. On the face of it, anyone who studies the B-1B will know a great deal about the new Soviet bomber, though the latter's greater size almost certainly translates into increased capability. It would be unwise to perpetuate the errors of past years and assume that Soviet designers are inferior and simply need larger hardware to fly the same mission.

Paris '83: Shuttle steals the show

Austin J. Brown

The Paris Salon of 1983 could have been just another foot-slogging air show, made all the more tiring by the knowledge that the Soviet decision not to exhibit aircraft had put paid to any hopes of seeing the eagerly awaited Antonov transport of C-5 Galaxy size. There was also to be no Rockwell B-1 to dominate Le Bourget as it did Farnborough in 1982. These letdowns were offset in part by the appearance of the very impressive F-20 Tigershark, conspicuous not only for its prowess in the air but also by the absence of many other US fighters, and the displays of the Sea Harrier, Tornado and the gamut of Mirages. But for many the entire show was made worthwhile by the presence of the US Space Shuttle Orbiter. This spacecraft-cum-aeroplane, atop its 747 carrier, was without doubt the star attraction of the show, although those with a mind for the future could not fail to have been impressed also by some of the mock-ups in the exhibition halls.

(All photographs by Austin J. Brown, except where credited otherwise.)

For a few days Le Bourget played host to the greatest variety of flying machines in the world, from microlights to spacecraft. (*Air Portraits*)

Above: **The new Bell 400 TwinRanger will have the advantage of its single-engined predecessor in being able to operate in instrument conditions. Note the shrouded tail rotor and four-blade main rotor.**

Left: **For many the unrivalled star of the show was Space Shuttle Orbiter** *Enterprise.*

Below left: **Double-deckers old and the new: the Space Shuttle Orbiter glimpsed between the wings of the Musée de l'Air's beautifully kept Breguet 14B2.**

Below: **Unmistakably Romanian in origin, the second Rombac 1-11 Series 560 was demonstrated for the first time at Paris.**

Left: **Northrop's F-20 Tigershark displayed great agility at Paris, trailing smoke and actively competing against the Mirage IIING in front of the international crowd. Chief test pilot Darrell Cornell's display reflected more than 3,000 flying hours on T-38s, F-5s and the F-20.**

Right: **Beechcraft's contender in the commuter market, the Beech 1900, will meet stiff opposition in Europe from aircraft like the Dornier 228 and British Aerospace Jetstream 31.**

Left: **David and Goliath: Boeing's Model 767 demonstrator holds to allow the Butterfly microlight to be pushed past.**

Below: **The striking blue-and-white** *Nouvelle Génération* **Mirage III prototype made its first public appearance at Paris, flying daily. Its fly-by-wire control system and foreplanes almost make a new aircraft out of the quarter-century-old Mirage design.**

Left: **An impressive display performer was the Nasa/Boeing QSRA (Quiet Short-haul Research Aircraft), converted at a cost of $21 million from a DHC Buffalo airframe.**

Below: **Paris was the first opportunity for the public to see the British Aerospace Hawk trainer in its latest guise, armed for anti-shipping strike with a Sea Eagle under the fuselage and two self-protection Sidewinders under the wings.** (*British Aerospace*)

Below: **One of three aircraft at the show currently being flown on liquid petroleum gas (LPG) was this homebuilt Piel CP-1320 Saphir, owned by Jean-Claude Lascoutounas and unusual in having a tricycle landing gear. The others were the Cessna 152 which Reims Aviation is certificating in association with Elf Petroleum, and the Socata Tobago which is being developed for LPG operation with Socata Primagaz, a system which has also been flight-tested on a Rallye 180.**

Right: **Robin's ATL lightweight trainer was displayed in the static park. It is powered by a specially developed 35kW (47hp) three-cylinder engine.**

Below: **The unusually configured Fairchild Republic FRC 225 full-spectrum trainer, designed as a replacement for the Cessna T-37, was displayed in full-scale mock-up form.**

Left: **The capabilities of the US Army's new UH-60A Black Hawk helicopter have been extended by the development of the detachable External Stores Support System (ESSS), which can be installed by four people in under 50min.**

Below: **The Saab-Fairchild 340 prototype taxis to the holding point for its display. The starboard side is painted in the colours of Air Midwest.**

Above: **Aero Maroc Industrie (AMI) showed this mock-up of its Gepal Mk III piston-engined trainer.**

Left: **The new General Electric-powered Canadair Challenger 601 was certificated by the FAA in March 1983 and appeared at Paris alongside a Swiss air ambulance version of the 600 series.**

Below: **The Gulfstream Aerospace Fanjet 1500, the world's only single-engined business jet, performed alongside the company's Peregrine 500 trainer.**

Gear for all seasons

Roy McLeavy

Since the earliest days of powered flight landing gear styles have changed almost as frequently as fashions in airframes. But despite the vast range conceived and used during the past 80 years, most aircraft use wheels, making them dependent on prepared runways or firm, flat surfaces. Examination of the entries in the current *Jane's All the World's Aircraft* reveals one surprising omission: despite the massive advances made in aerodynamic design, powerplants, aircraft structures and avionics since the beginning of the jet age, no aircraft with a multi-terrain undercarriage has yet reached production status.

Awareness of the attractions of such an aircraft is nowhere greater than in Canada, where Bell Aerospace Canada Textron (BACT) and the Department of Industry, Trade and Commerce (DIT & C) are jointly developing a craft known as the Light Air Cushion Triphibious Aircraft (LACTA). The objective is to combine the speed, capacity and range of a contemporary light aircraft with the multi-terrain mobility of an air-cushion vehicle, thus liberating the aircraft from its dependence on runways.

Aircraft employing LACTA landing gear technology will effectively be a completely new form of transport. Until now aircraft have been equipped with either wheels, skis, floats, a monohull, a monohull and wheels, or a twin hull. Never before has there been a single system that combines the capabilities of them all. An air-cushion landing gear (ACLG) minimises airstrip requirements and enables aircraft to take off from and land on any flat, unprepared surface: water, land, snow, ice, marsh, sand, mud and even ploughed fields. It also enables pilots to make safe and controlled crosswind take-offs and landings.

ACLG-equipped aircraft are also attractive to air forces and air freight specialists operating very large transports, the use of which is restricted by the inability of many runways to bear their weight. Moreover, currently projected giant freight aircraft with all-up weights in excess of 1,000 tonnes would be able to take off and land with much heavier loads than could possibly be borne by conventional multi-wheel undercarriages.

In addition, large freight aircraft with ACLG would no longer have to use conventional airports, thereby relieving some of the pressure created by the continuing growth in world air traffic. Regular freight services could be operated to the many Third World countries which cannot afford to build conventional airports to international standards, but which possess suitable stretches of land that could be prepared by bulldozers. As concrete runways and taxiways would be virtually eliminated, almost the only form of construction necessary would be the provision of aprons for loading and offloading freight.

An air-cushion aircraft could provide an economical year-round transport service in northern Canada, where there are areas which in winter are totally inaccessible even to tracked vehicles, ACVs and dog sleds. A "triphibian" could fly over mountain ranges, pressure ridges and broken ice floes and land on any strip of relatively flat ice or firm, snow-covered terrain. Since in most cases supplies and equipment would be delivered virtually to where they were needed, ground handling and additional transport costs would be very much reduced.

How close is LACTA to being a commercial reality? Given the necessary funding, the prototype/demonstrator could be airborne within three to four years, possibly sooner. The practicability of ACLG was first demonstrated by a converted Lake LA-4 single-engine light amphibian in 1967.

Development of the idea began at Bell Aerospace Canada Textron in 1964, under the direction of Desmond Earl and his colleague Wilfrid J. Eggington. Earl had started his own ACLG experiments in the early 1950s when working on the projected Avro Avrocar Vtol supersonic fighter, which was to have had an air-cushion landing gear. The triple-jet Avrocar, which proved to be too exotic for its time and too difficult to control, was cancelled, but further concepts calling for the blending of air-cushion and aircraft technology were under consideration when Avro Canada shut its doors in 1959.

Earl later joined Bell Aerospace at Niagara Falls, New York, and together with Eggington set to work to

devise an ACLG which would permit amphibious operation. In 1964 the pair designed a system based on an elastic, doughnut-shaped bag. Bell patented the design in 1965, with Earl and Eggington named as co-inventors. A Lake LA-4 fitted with such a landing system performed its first take-off and landing in September 1967, operating in 40km/hr (25mph) winds on Lake Erie. It needed only 200m (650ft) of water for take-off and 76m (250ft) for landing. Afterwards it demonstrated its amphibious capabilities by taxiing ashore. A long series of tests followed, during which the LA-4 showed it could perform well on grass, ice, snow and water and was not averse to taxiing across mud and ploughed fields.

The ACLG on the LA-4 performs all the functions of a conventional undercarriage. On landing, six brake skids on the underside of the air-cushion trunk are brought into contact with the surface by inflating pneumatic pillows. When parking on land or water a lightweight bladder inside the trunk seals the airjets, supporting the aircraft at rest on land or providing it with buoyancy to keep it afloat on water. On all improved surfaces the ACLG LA-4 is easier to control than would be the case with a wheeled landing gear, and the performance is problem-free on surfaces which make the use of wheels impossible. According to pilots, the aircraft's ability to make safe and controlled landings in high crosswinds is outstanding. It is also less sensitive to landings carried out at the wrong attitude and with high descent rates at touchdown.

The next major stage in the development of ACLG began in 1970, when the US Air Force saw the possibility of applying the idea to a tactical transport aircraft, giving it the ability to fly into and out of front-line airfields. In November 1970 a joint US/Canadian prog-

ramme was set up to demonstrate the capabilities of an ACLG-equipped transport aircraft. The Canadian Department of National Defence lent the project a DHC CC-115 Buffalo transport, which was designated XC-8A by the USAF. de Havilland Aircraft of Canada modified the aircraft for the ACLG system, United Aircraft of Canada developed two ST6F-70 gas-turbine fan systems to supply air to the ACLG, and Bell supplied the landing trunk, which was an enlarged version of that used on the experimental LA-4. Flight trials began in mid-1974. Although the XC-8A took off and landed on its air cushion many times, the tests were considered only a limited success. The XC-8A was very much bigger and more sophisticated than the LA-4, and a large part of the funds allocated was eaten up by its operation and maintenance. It was also concluded that too great a step had been attempted after the LA-4 trials, particularly in view of the problems encountered in trying at so early a stage to modify an existing aircraft to incorporate an ACLG.

In 1971 a USAF decision to investigate the possibility of fitting ACLG to high-performance jet aircraft resulted in the modification by Bell of an Australian Jindivik drone. Air bled from the Jindivik's Viper gas turbine inflated the landing trunk, but otherwise the system was almost identical with though smaller than that used on the XC-8A. The modifications were carried out at Wright-Patterson Air Force Base, after which the craft was taken to Australia for flight trials which satisfactorily demonstrated the feasibility of high-speed flight and landing with ACLG.

Subsequently, a further Bell study, carried out in conjunction with other major US aerospace companies, showed that ACLG (known for the purposes of this study as a Surface Effect Take-Off and Landing sys-

Far left: **The Lake LA-4 demonstrating during trials its ability to maintain a track along the runway centreline.** (*Bell*)

Left: **Modified Buffalo fitted with ACLG for tests by the US Air Force Flight Dynamics Laboratory.**

Below: **Artist's impression of an ACLG-equipped Buffalo operating from terrain unsuitable for aircraft with conventional wheeled landing gear.** (*Bell*)

tem, SETOL) would permit a single naval aircraft design to perform a variety of roles formerly calling for a land-based aircraft, a carrier-based aircraft and a seaplane. Although flight trials with the various modified production craft proved beyond doubt the practicality of the ACLG, it was evident that to perfect the concept it would be necessary to design and build an aircraft matched to the system from the outset.

Earl's next step was therefore to prepare an outline LACTA design. Seating eight, LACTA will have a wider fuselage than the LA-4 to accommodate a large-area, wide-track ovoid air-cushion trunk. It will be a low-wing monoplane with twin tail booms and will be powered by a 298 kW (400 hp) Lycoming piston engine mounted above the fuselage on a pylon and driving a 208.3cm (82in)-diameter three-blade Hartzell propeller. Dihedral of 10° on the centre section of the 9.75m (32ft) span wings provides stability when operating on water, and wingtip fuel tanks give additional buoyancy.

First objective of this new programme is to prove beyond doubt that the air-cushion landing gear will work efficiently and cost no more to operate than a conventional wheeled gear. During this stage the converted ACLG LA-4 will be taken out of storage at Buffalo and shipped to Grand Bend to be used as a testbed for the LACTA landing gear. J. & V. Nash, a company which builds fibreglass yachts and compo-

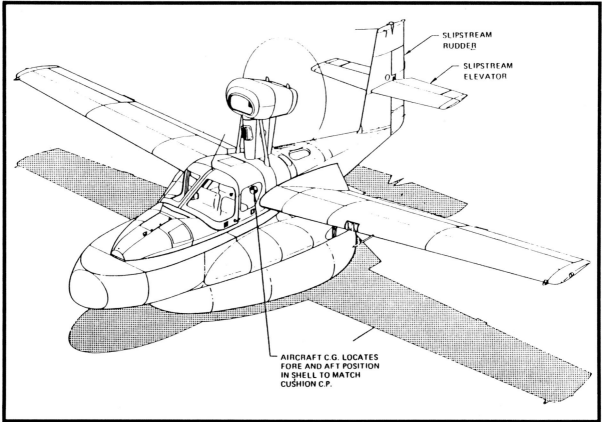

SLIPSTREAM RUDDER

SLIPSTREAM ELEVATOR

AIRCRAFT C.G. LOCATES FORE AND AFT POSITION IN SHELL TO MATCH CUSHION C.P.

Above: **Artist's impression of the Light Air Cushion Triphibious Aircraft (LACTA).**

Left: **Drawing of the LA-4 equipped with LACTA air-cushion trunk.**

Below right: **UT-2 equipped with an air-cushion landing gear designed by Robert Oros di Bartini.**

nents for the US Army's LACV-30 programme, is to construct a ply-and-fibreglass LACTA ventral fuselage to fit onto the LA-4. Incorporated in the fuselage will be the LACTA landing gear, which will be tested by taxiing the LA-4 over the same kind of surfaces which it proved capable of crossing during its earlier trials programme. Although this initial phase does not include flight testing, the LA-4 has been restored to flying condition and could take to the air if it is decided to extend the programme.

LACTA's doughnut-shaped air-cushion trunk is made from an elastic tape based on recycled rubber tyre cord. A hydraulic pump driven by the main engine forces air into the trunk, which is perforated on its underside with more than 2,000 small holes through which most of the air escapes to provide both an air cushion and lubrication between the trunk and the surface beneath. The remaining holes are plugged with hard-wearing chlorobutyl rubber and are brought into contact with the surface on landing to produce a braking effect. The elasticity of the trunk ensures that it snaps tightly against the underside of the fuselage in flight, and the drag penalty is negligible.

Design of the complete LACTA craft continues in parallel with this effort, together with market research and assessments of aerodynamic and hydrodynamic performance. Assistance with research and development is also being given by various Canadian government departments: the National Research Council is conducting wind-tunnel tests; the Department of Transport is advising on aspects of air-cushion vehicle operation and requirements for an airworthiness certificate; the Department of Defence is providing information on the use of advanced composite materials; and the Department of Trade, Industry and Commerce is providing funds and co-ordinates government involvement.

Before the second stage can begin, BACT must find a partner with airframe construction experience and a working knowledge of aircraft systems. Although a number of Canadian companies qualify, various other factors could lead to a joint venture with a foreign company.

The triphibian (and a range of enlarged derivatives) should have a highly beneficial effect on communications the world over, but especially in the outback areas. In the hinterlands of Third World countries, where traditional vehicles are unable to cope with the climatic, terrain and soil conditions, it would provide a fast, reliable link with main transport networks. In underdeveloped areas it could help to solve acute economic problems by assisting in the exploitation of new energy, mineral and food resources, while its potential for disaster relief work is enormous.

None of this is lost upon the Soviet Union, which has vast tracts of territory that are only now being opened up. Canada's ACLG programme is being watched with keen interest in the USSR, where experiments with this type of undercarriage are said to have begun in 1939. Flight tests were first carried out with a UT-2 basic trainer in which the ACLG was fitted beneath the wing centre-section. A fan powered by an 18kW (24hp) motorcycle engine forced air into the air cushion bag.

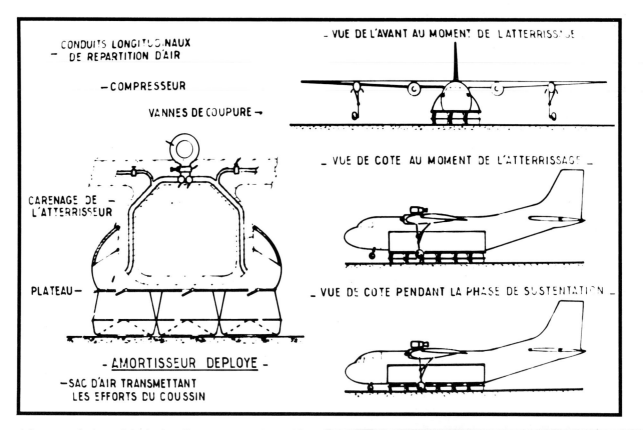

CONDUITS LONGITUDINAUX DE REPARTITION D'AIR

COMPRESSEUR

VANNES DE COUPURE →

CARENAGE DE L'ATTERRISSEUR

PLATEAU

- AMORTISSEUR DEPLOYE -

SAC D'AIR TRANSMETTANT LES EFFORTS DU COUSSIN

VUE DE L'AVANT AU MOMENT DE L'ATTERRISSAGE

VUE DE COTE AU MOMENT DE L'ATTERRISSAGE

VUE DE COTE PENDANT LA PHASE DE SUSTENTATION

After completing trials the landing gear was adopted in 1941 for a reconnaissance version of the Pe-2 twin-engined bomber. Further development was interrupted by the outbreak of war.

Recently interest in this form of landing gear appears to have been revived by the Soviet Air Force, and publicity has been given to tests involving the mounting of ACLG test sensors on an Il-14 transport equipped with skis.

The late Jean Bertin, former head of Société Bertin & Cie, was also active in this field. In 1962 he patented an ACLG based on his technique of separately fed multiple plenum chambers. The system was designed to enable the then projected Bertin Cygne series of 1,000-tonne-plus free-flying/surface-effect aircraft not only to take off and land with far heavier loads than can be borne by conventional wheeled arrangements but also to permit them to operate from both land and water.

Another of Bertin's inventions is the Atérroglisseur, designed to prevent heavy loads dropped by parachute from turning over on landing. As the load platform lands, balloons beneath it cushion the impact in a controlled deflation. Air from the balloons is then fed into a series of multiple skirts, inflating them and creating an air cushion. This allows the platform to skim the surface in the dropping zone, giving the parachutes time to settle and so reducing the possibility of the load overturning. As the skirts are flattened, increased friction through surface contact brings the platform to a halt.

Two other important areas in which aerospace and

Top: **Drawings of the Bertin air-cushion landing gear.** (*Bertin*)

Above: **Bertin air-cushion pads moving a jet engine along an assembly line.**

Top right: **Tripods fitted with Bertin air-cushion pads are being used to position this Air France Airbus A300.**

Centre right: **Atérroglisseur air-cushion-supported load platform, designed to prevent heavy loads dropped by parachute from overturning when landing.** (*Bertin*)

air-cushion technology meet are industrial handling and aircraft recovery. Compact air pallets are being used in their thousands in Europe and the United States to speed the movement of complete aircraft, components and engines through assembly lines and to assist in manoeuvring airliners of all sizes within the confined spaces of maintenance hangars. In the US Space Shuttle programme air pallets are used from the first phase of production to the final recovery. Air-transportable aircraft recovery systems are being built in the United Kingdom and Canada. A disabled aircraft can be moved from the runway, or retrieved from ground which cannot be negotiated by conventional vehicles, by lifting it with pneumatic elevators or jacks and then supporting it on hover platforms while it is towed away. Supported by an air pressure of less than $0.07 kg/cm^2$ ($1 lb/in^2$), it can be hovered across all types of terrain, leaving the ground surface undisturbed.

Below: **Aircraft recovery system built in the United Kingdom by Aero-Docks Ltd of Southampton.**

Woodbridge Warthogs at work

T. J. Gander

Although the Fairchild Republic A-10A Thunderbolt II first flew during 1972, it was not until 1979 that the type became operational with the 81st Tactical Fighter Wing in the UK on its first overseas deployment. The wing was completely converted to the type by September 1981, by which time it comprised no fewer than six squadons. Today the wing is based at two adjacent airfields, RAF Bentwaters and RAF Woodbridge, close to the Suffolk coast. RAF Bentwaters is the home of the 92nd Tactical Fighter Squadron ("The Avengers"), the 509th TFS ("The Pirates"), the 510th TFS ("The Buzzards") and the 511th TFS ("The Vultures"). RAF Woodbridge is the home base of the 78th TFS ("The Bushmasters") and the 91st TFS ("The Blue Streaks").

The 91st TFS invited the author to spend a working day with them, and the following photographs are the result. The Blue Streaks were happy to show off the A-10A, which they have affectionately named the "Warthog". They are kept very busy (the wing flew no fewer than 53,000hr in 1982), flying either from their Suffolk bases or from the Forward Operating Locations (FOLs) at Leipheim, Ahlhorn, Sembach and Norvenheim in Germany. In time of war the 81st TFW would be divided between 2ATAF and 4ATAF. With their Maverick missiles and potent 30mm GAU-8/A Avenger cannon the Warthogs would be a deadly threat to any invading tank formation.

(All photographs by T. J. Gander. Warthog drawing by Hank Caruso appears by permission of the 81st TFW.)

Warthog at work. (*Hank Caruso*)

Below: **Early-morning pre-flight briefing for Igloo 25, 26 and 27 or (from left to right) Capt Steve Anderson (the flight leader), Capt Ron Juhl and Lt John Liberto. Their mission lasted nearly 2hr, involving a low-level navigation exercise, a simulated attack on a small bridge and a gun-firing attack on a towed target off Lowestoft. The briefing for the mission lasted more than an hour.**

Above: **The business end of the Warthog, showing the prominent muzzles of the 30mm GAU-8/A cannon. The flat panel in front of the canopy hides the in-flight refuelling receptacle. The large engines make for easy recognition of the A-10A: Suffolk locals know the aircraft as "the aeroplane with the two dustbins on the back."**

Right: **Capt Steve Anderson carrying out pre-flight checks with the aircraft still in its Hardened Aircraft Shelter (HAS). The engines are started inside the HAS.**

Left: The final pre-flight checks are carried out once the aircraft has taxied out of the HAS. The groundcrew check man remains in communication with the pilot throughout. All the control surfaces are actuated, and even the pitot head heater is checked — by hand.

Below: Igloo 25 taxies out to the end of the runway with the cockpit canopy still up.

Bottom: Igloo 26 (Lt John Liberto) takes off from Woodbridge's massively wide runway. The station was originally built as a recovery base for damaged British and Allied aircraft, and the runway is about five times as wide as normal. Only the centre strip is now used. This aircraft is carrying an ALQ-119 ECM pod under the port wing.

Right: The mission complete, rearming begins with the pilot still in the cockpit. The aircraft is winched back into its HAS and the APU is started to provide power for the operation, which includes reloading the 30mm gun with the Automatic Loading System (ALS) seen in the foreground.

Left: **Capt Steve Anderson completes his after-flight documentation. He is using a fire-extinguisher trolley as a desk.**

Below: **Close-up of the ALS trolley for the 30mm gun. The linkage closest to the camera takes the ammunition from cases on a trolley, in which they are contained in white plastic collars. In the ALS the rounds are removed from the collars and passed into the gun system.**

Right: **The business end of the ALS. The operation is complicated by the fact that the empty 30mm cartridge cases have to be removed from the gun's internal drum magazine as the new rounds are fed in, hence the twin chains of linkages.**

Left: **Preparing the feed-in head of the ALS for attachment to the aircraft. The crewman is wearing ear defenders as protection against the high noise level inside the HAS when the aircraft APU is running and the ALS is in full swing.**

Right: **The ALS in full operation. Rounds can be seen inside the linkages in the foreground, and the ammunition boxes can be seen at the rear. The boxes are filled with spent cases as the new rounds in their collars are taken out.**

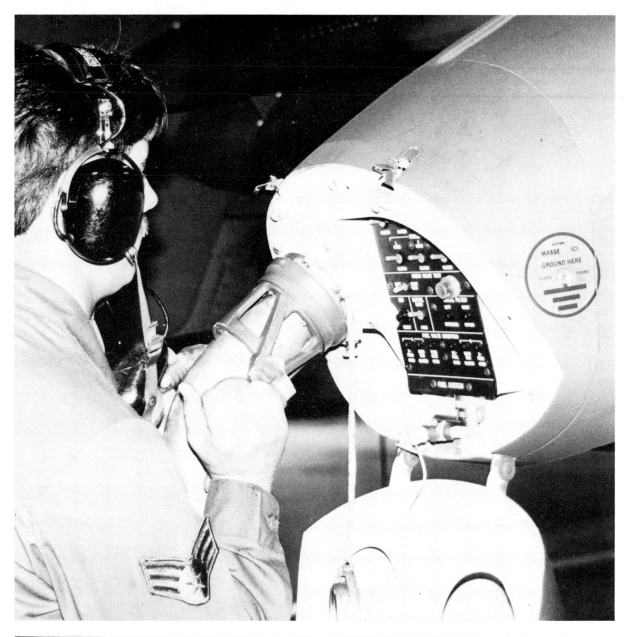

Left: **Removing a Maverick missile from its container before placing it on a self-propelled loading trolley with an articulated arm. This is a training round, with only the video camera and pointing system fitted in the nose and connected to a cockpit screen.**

Left: **The single refuelling point of the A-10A is positioned inside the pod on the port wing. The HAS is large enough for the tanker to drive inside, and refuelling is carried out with the large armoured doors fully closed.**

Right: **Loading the Maverick onto the first outboard underwing pylon. Early versions of the A-10A have pylons able to carry three Mavericks each, but these are now being replaced by single-point pylons to reduce drag. In future most missions will be carried out with only two Mavericks and a full 30mm ammunition load.**

Centre right: **The final line-up of the Maverick on the pylon. Reloading and refuelling are carried out together to minimise turnround times.**

Below: **Outside the HAS more aircraft are ready to move out. The flat plate beneath the cockpit of this aircraft is a pylon for the Pave Penny laser-designation pod, which receives signals reflected from illuminated targets. If the signals come from the area in front of the aircraft, this is indicated on the pilot's head-up display (HUD).**

Below: **At RAF Woodbridge the men of the 581st Aircraft Generation Squadron are responsible for keeping the Blue Streaks airborne. Their work includes basic checks such as the undercarriage inspection being carried out by this airframe mechanic.**

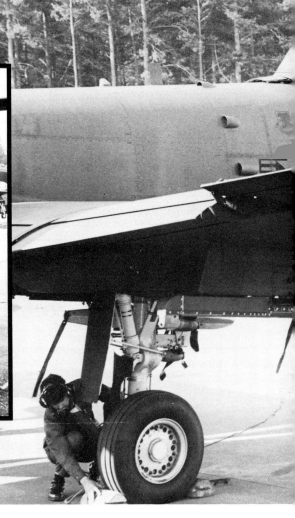

Right: **More pre-flight checks. Note the profusion of warning flags fluttering under the aircraft.**

Below: **The AN/ALQ-119 ECM pod, which is used to jam enemy electronics and radars. Warthogs are now being fitted with Have Quick frequency-hopping radios capable of evading enemy communications jamming.**

Below: **Another Warthog take-off. The colour scheme used by the 81st TFW is very effective against the North European landscape, and some pilots have said that it blends so well with the terrain that only a sudden move by the aircraft will betray its position.**

Above: **RAF Woodbridge is constantly patrolled inside its perimeter by special security personnel. This guard is armed with an M15 5.56mm rifle fitted with a grenade launcher. The vehicle, a Cadillac Gage Commando Ranger armoured personnel carrier, can mount an M60 7.62mm machine gun on its roof.**

Left: **The cockpit of the A-10A is a long way from the ground. Each aircraft has an integral stepladder located behind a panel beneath the cockpit.**

Below: **Off on another mission. The Warthogs have demonstrated in exercises their ability to fly sortie "surges" of the magnitude that would be demanded in war.**

Luscombe Rattler: the ultralight with bite

David Mondey

Looking around in 1970 for a suitable project to get his teeth into, ex-Royal Navy pilot Patrick Luscombe decided that there was room for a lightweight and inexpensive two-seat trainer with foolproof flight characteristics. His own flying experience had shown that the bill could not be filled easily by an aircraft of traditional configuration, so in 1971 he designed an ultralight two-seater of canard layout. The resulting prototype showed great promise and was followed by an improved version, the Vitality. Extensive flight testing of these two aircraft led to the construction of a third in 1981, which emerged as the prototype Luscombe Valiant. Since it was first flown, in September 1982, two further examples have been built, and it is planned to use all three to gain type certification by 1984. The company has agencies in both Japan and the United States which are negotiating to clear the way for imports of the Valiant.

During flight tests Luscombe realised the military potential of his aircraft and started work on the design of a single-seat version. This combines the basic Vitality airframe with a new glassfibre wing developed specifically for the military variant. Generally similar in size and configuration to the Vitality, the new aircraft, known as the Luscombe P3 Rattler, is powered by the highest-rated of the three different engines which can be fitted to the Valiant. This is the 60kW (80hp) Weslake 65/80-118-2 flat-four engine, driving a two-blade fixed-pitch wooden pusher propeller. A Hoffmann variable-pitch propeller will also be available as an option.

Flight tests of the Rattler prototype, together with those of the Vitality and Valiant, had given the company more than 1,300hr of flight experience by early 1983, leading to the current pre-production Rattler (G-BKPG). The type is intended to perform a variety of

The current pre-production Luscombe P3 Rattler, G-BKPG, could be the first of a new breed of military aircraft.

roles near the forward edge of the battlefield, and this has dictated one of the leading features of the design. The wings can be removed easily for storage or towing, and there is a special trailer to carry the aircraft with the wings stowed alongside the fuselage; the whole load can be towed without difficulty by a light vehicle. This capability, and other easy breakdown and re-erection features of the P3 design, are seen as vital in a military aircraft of this class, permitting it to be transported quickly in a disassembled state, by air or land, to the operational area. On arrival it could be reassembled by semi-skilled labour in little more than 15min, and once completed could take off from a road or grass strip after ground runs of 46m (150ft) and 61m (200ft) respectively.

The survivability of a manned version of the Rattler in a hostile environment remains to be proven. However potent the armament it may be able to carry, the difference between the aircraft's dry empty weight and its maximum take-off weight of 454 kg (1,000lb) is only 263kg (580lb). If from this figure you subtract the weight of a pilot, 45lit (10 Imp gal) of fuel, a Hughes Chain Gun, 2,000 rounds of ammunition and six 2in air-to-ground rockets, it is clear that no significant armour protection can be given to the pilot. "You can punch it [the Rattler] full of holes and it will keep on flying," according to Luscombe, but its pilot must be far more vulnerable.

There seems to be a way round this problem, however. Luscombe is working on a package which will convert the Rattler into a remotely piloted vehicle. Thus configured, the Rattler could operate as an observation platform, carrying a conventional or TV camera and a variety of electronic pods capable of jamming radar and performing a number of other ECM roles.

While no definitive armament fit can be selected until there is an opportunity for flight tests of the various proposals, possible weapons include a 7.62mm Hughes Chain Gun with 2,000 rounds of ammunition, unguided 2in air-to-ground rockets carried in two seven-round launchers, one beneath each wing, or two Ranger four-tube anti-personnel mine dispensers mounted one under each wing and able to launch a total of 144 mines. To minimise centre-of-gravity problems the Chain Gun would be mounted as high as possible on the starboard side of the fuselage so that its magazine could be within the fuselage, behind the pilot's seat. This position would ensure minimal trim changes as the magazine emptied.

At its maximum take-off weight the production Rattler would be able to become airborne at a speed of only 68km/hr (42mph), and have a maximum sea-level speed of 160km/hr (100mph) and an economic cruising speed of 145km/hr (90mph). Its large, lightly loaded wing would permit sustained flight at altitudes in excess of 4,570m (15,000ft), and the maximum capacity of 181lit (40 Imp gal) of fuel would give a duration of 11hr. Coupled with a price tag of around £15,000, this must mean that Rattler is worthy of serious consideration as a cheap and easily operated battlefield RPV. The company claims that it has the fire-support capability of a light armed helicopter, while its £15,000 cost means that for the cost of just one helicopter a hard-up air force could acquire some 60 Rattlers. Operating costs are in proportion.

Luscombe sells the Rattler hard, claiming that it is far less vulnerable than a helicopter, can operate on Mogas, demands much less in the way of pilot training and, given suitable armament, could pack a formidable punch. One unspecified Arab nation is so impressed that it is said to be interested in acquiring some 400 examples. Rattler's abilities remain to be proven, however, and only extensive testing and evaluation will provide the answers.

Luscombe Rattler data

Wing span	12.19m (40ft)
Length overall	4.57m (15ft)
Height overall	1.83m (6ft)
Foreplane span	2.29m (7ft 6in)
Propeller diameter	1.47m (4ft 10in)
Wing area	13.66m² (147.0ft²)
g limits	+6/−3

Special shapes and Bristol-fashion

Peter J. Bish

A French chateau, a packet of cigarettes, five assorted bottles, two pairs of jeans, a goofy hare, an oil drum, a Pakistani minaret, a beer barrel, a sparkplug, two cottages, a paint pot, a lightbulb, an ancient gas balloon and a pipe: what, you may ask, do these objects have in common? Simple: throw in a couple of advertising characters ("Golly" and the Planter's peanut man) and you have the incredible fleet of special-shape hot-air balloons built to date by Cameron Balloons Ltd of Bristol. But they are not simply outsize advertising gimmicks. Each one is a fully engineered free-flying balloon, complete with a certificate of airworthiness and flown extensively for promotional purposes worldwide.

Cameron is undoubtedly the world leader in this area of balloon construction, having exported such shapes throughout Europe and to the USA, Canada, Pakistan and Hong Kong. Since the formation of Cameron Balloons Ltd in 1970 the company has also built over 800 conventionally shaped hot-air balloons and airships, over two-thirds of which have been exported. Cameron's products are registered in no fewer than 25 countries.

Construction of the special shapes follows the same basic principles embodied in standard balloons. But where odd projections which are needed for the shape cannot be used to generate lift (the arms of the men, the lower left trouser leg of the jeans, etc), these are connected to the main body of the balloon so that they fill with cold air and are kept under just enough pressure to maintain their shape. Bracing tapes and wires are used within the cavernous interiors to hold in flat or concave surfaces.

(All photographs by Peter J. Bish, except where otherwise credited.)

Golly III (G-OLLI) and *Erinmore* (G-PIPE) caught having a quick smoke behind the trees of Ashton Court, Avon. (*Cameron Balloons Ltd*)

The first of two 1,699m³ (60,000ft³) cottages built by Cameron belongs to the Nottingham Building Society. It first flew from Ashton Court, Avon, on February 1, 1981, as G-HOUS, a registration already allocated to a Colt 31A, and so was registered as G-COTT shortly afterwards. The second cottage, G-BKEO, has been exported to Canada. *(Cameron Balloons Ltd)*

The Seura hare was the symbol of the 1983 World Athletics Championships, held in Finland. The hare (OH-JBT) is seen taking off from Ashton Court, Avon, on its maiden flight. (*Cameron Balloons Ltd*)

Undoubtedly the largest bottle in the world, and certainly one of the few to fly, the Robinsons Orange Barley Water bottle (G-BKES) was built during 1982 for operators Lighter-Than-Air Ltd. (*Cameron Balloons Ltd*)

Far left: **This oil drum (G-BHTM) could take some 404,800gal if it was not filled with hot air. The balloon promotes BP at many agricultural shows throughout the UK. It took off on its maiden flight from the Bath and West Show at Shepton Mallet, Somerset, on May 30, 1980.** (*Cameron Balloons Ltd*)

Left: **Bottles are popular amongst special-shape advertisers. This 1,586m³ (56,000ft³) Bisquit brandy bottle (G-VSOP) is based in Hong Kong. It is seen here on its maiden free flight from Ashton Court, Avon, on June 3, 1982.** (*Cameron Balloons Ltd*)

Below left: **Most ambitious special shape so far tackled by Cameron is the 2,379m³ (84,000ft³) replica of publisher Malcolm Forbes' Chateau de Balleroy (G-BKBR). The pilot of this giant must have a restricted upward view from his position in the cellar! The European hot-air balloon championship at Warken, Luxembourg, last year was the occasion of the balloon's maiden free flight.** (*Cameron Balloons Ltd*)

Right: **With an inside leg measurement of 1,198in, this is surely the largest pair of trousers ever! Based in Holland, this balloon (G-BREN) is sponsored by C&A to promote its jeans. The left leg is sealed at the base, the basket and burner assembly being suspended below the right leg. Surprisingly, even with this weight distribution, the jeans fly level in free flight. G-BREN is seen here during a test inflation at Marsh Benham, Berks, on June 1, 1979.**

Left: **Another ambitious shape, the 991m³ (35,000ft³) Champion sparkplug (G-BETF) was built in 1977. With a height of over 100ft, it soon proved unflyable in anything other than calm, stable conditions. Even the slightest windshear would produce bending of the narrow upper part of the balloon as it tried to move with the higher airstream.**

Right: **The Osram lightbulb is a relatively natural special shape. It is especially effective when inflated at night, the illuminated interior creating the effect of a real light bulb. Osram (G-BEWS) is now based in Australia.** (*Roger Kunert*)

Above: **One of the more obscure objects reproduced by Cameron is Engineering Appliances' expansion joint (G-BIUL). Like the lightbulb, it is much more akin to a proper balloon shape and is relatively easy to fly. It is seen here at the Bristol International Balloon Fiesta at Ashton Court, Avon, in August 1982.**

Above right: **Charles Wells Ales sponsors this brown-and-silver 3½ million-pint barrel (G-PINT), seen here taking off from the Thunder Meet, University of East Anglia, Norwich, in September 1982.**

Right: **Following several conventionally shaped balloons, Porter Paints of the USA took delivery of this yellow-and-orange-striped paint can (N56PP) in 1978.** (Cameron Balloons Ltd)

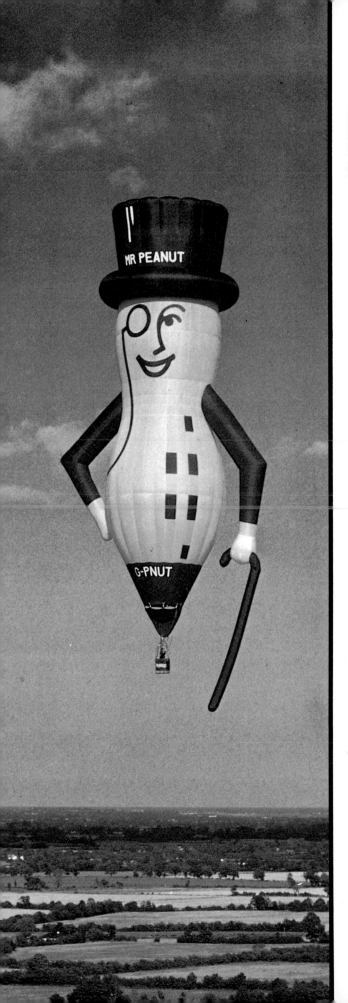

Above: **One of the more tricky shapes to fly, due to its enormous slab sides and the effect of the slightest wind upon them, is the 1,699m³ (60,000ft³) Winston cigarette packet (G-BHJV). Originally based in Hong Kong,** *Winston* **is now in Spain following changes in the colony's cigarette advertising laws.** (*Cameron Balloons Ltd*)

Left: *Mr Peanut* **(G-PNUT) is one of identical 991m³ (35,000ft³) twins operated by Balloon Stable Ltd. G-PNUT was transferred to the USA as N400AB during 1982, while G-NUTS is currently based in South Africa.** (*Balloon Stable Ltd*)

Eurofighter: faint hope or fighting chance?

Mike Hirst

Europe has as many military aircraft manufacturers as the US but only a fraction of the opportunity to build in quantity. A new collaborative fighter is needed soon and would give the European planemakers a chance to enjoy the benefits of long production runs. But there is a problem, one that will be familiar to any student of European aerospace collaboration. There are already in existence one international and two national fighter projects, and their protagonists are still determinedly going their separate ways. Even so, although the difficulties of combining these three efforts look formidable, there is good reason to believe that they will be overcome and that Eurofighter will be the next great collaborative venture. The risks are high, however, and the necessary realignment of the European industry might just result in casualties among the partner companies.

Around 3,600 supersonic strike/fighter aircraft are currently based in Western Europe. Many of them are earmarked for retirement by 1990, and they will be

replaced by the Viggens, Tornadoes and Mirages that are in production in Sweden, Britain, West Germany, Italy and France. The number of aircraft operated by these countries will diminish only slightly as a result of this re-equipment. About half of all the supersonic aircraft in Europe came from the United States, which will continue to supply a large proportion in the future. The McDonnell Douglas F-4 Phantom, Lockheed F-104 Starfighter and Northrop F-5 are the most numerous American types in European service. Many aircraft were supplied at knock-down rates in US foreign aid sales, coming either directly from production lines or from USAF surplus or reserve stocks.

Spain, Greece and Turkey, for instance, have sizeable fleets acquired in this way. Although they have small numbers of European aircraft on strength, the air forces of Belgium, Denmark, the Netherlands and Norway are re-equipping almost exclusively with the American-designed General Dynamics F-16 Fighting Falcon, while Spain has ordered the McDonnell Douglas F-18 Hornet. Clearly, the degree of US penetration of the European military aircraft market is unlikely to change greatly for some time to come.

All this adds up to a gloomy picture for European manufacturers in the 1990s. In 1975 there were about 1,850 supersonic aircraft in service with the major

Above left: **Current European needs are being met largely by the tri-national Tornado programme. Of the 805-aircraft total, most are for the interdictor-strike role, as shown here. The project was launched in 1969 and deliveries are due to be completed by 1990.** (BAe)

Above: **The Royal Air Force will take delivery of 165 air-defence Tornadoes to replace McDonnell Douglas F-4K/M Phantoms and BAC Lightnings from the mid-1980s. This long-endurance type is designed for combat air patrol and does not meet the need for a European close combat aircraft.** (BAe)

Left: **US-designed aircraft make up half of Europe's supersonic force. The General Dynamics F-16 Fighting Falcon spearheads current efforts by the US industry to hold on to this proportion of the market.**

Right: **Sweden's once unorthodox Viggen seems to have set the trend in supersonic fighter configurations. This is an example of the Sky Flash/Sidewinder-equipped JA37 all-weather fighter version.** (Saab)

European combat aircraft manufacturing nations: Britain, France, West Germany, Italy and Sweden. Even if this figure remains as high as 1,600 in the year 2000, some 1,200 of these aircraft are already being produced or are due to be, and mostly before 1990. If the traditional allegiance to the US industry remains strong throughout Europe, that leaves a home market for only 400 aircraft during 1990-2000.

The obvious solution to the problems posed by a limited domestic market is to seek more customers in other parts of the world. Within Europe there are nations such as Spain, Greece and Turkey which have aspiring aerospace industries, and it is just possible that their governments could be dissuaded from US purchases if enough in the way of partnership and financial offsets were offered. Assuming that 50 per cent of the likely US aircraft sales to Europe during 1990-2000 was secured in this way, the total home market would then amount to about 770 aircraft for, say, seven nations. This would generate a multi-national effort comparable with the Tornado programme, which was set up to produce 805 aircraft for three nations over a similar period.

Although the analysis thus far isn't promising, there is still the rest of the world to consider. Outside Europe there is a potential market during 1990-2000 for 4,000 or so aircraft in the same category as a European-developed fighter/strike type. If a European consortium could win 30 per cent of this (which would represent a market shift similar to that created by Airbus Industrie in the commercial field), a 2,000-aircraft production run would be a possibility. Given a production rate of 200 units a year, that is the sort of run that would keep the European industry happy. While it would

undoubtedly be very difficult to combine so many partners in such a venture, there can be no question of doing Eurofighter any other way: none of the above could work if even one of the current independent programmes set itself up in opposition.

If the size of the programme seems to present some thorny problems, now consider the timescale. If Europe is to have the aircraft available in time, it has only seven years in which to set up a multi-national organisation, sign formal work-sharing agreements and co-ordinate a dispersed team of engineers while they design, build, test and prepare for production one of the most advanced aircraft in the world. By comparison, the tri-national Tornado programme took 11 years

to cover the same ground, and Jaguar, a much less ambitious project with only two participants, took a little over seven years. The task is not at present impossible, but the time when it will be is approaching rapidly.

The three embryos which could be turned into Eurofighter are ACA (Advanced Combat Aircraft), a joint effort by Britain, West Germany and Italy, France's ACX, and the Swedish Gripen. Even though it has the best chance of being ready on time, the diminutive Gripen seems likely to be ruled out because it would be rejected by the majority of the European air forces within Nato as being too small for the roles they have in mind.

That leaves ACA and ACX. Both twin-engined, they are similar in size and power. Both have a delta mainplane and canard control surfaces and will embody fly-by-wire flight control systems. Both are single-seaters optimised as fighters but with respectable secondary strike characteristics. Both are said to be on

target for a 1986 first flight, and a 1990 first delivery. Neither design team talks to the other, however, though it is not that they haven't tried. During 1980-81 tri-national studies were supported by the defence ministries of Britain, France and West Germany. These efforts, directed towards a project provisionally called ECA (European Combat Aircraft), came to nothing because there was insufficient governmental pressure on the partners to find common ground.

Dassault, having invested substantially in the Mirage 4000, saw that aircraft or a derivative as the best starting point, while the West German engineers were already committed to the idea of a radically better fighter slightly smaller and far more agile than the Mirage 4000 is ever likely to be. Britain leaned in the same direction but made less of a case for agility at high angles of attack. The British team might have been able to inspire a compromise but could not hope to do so in the absence of some governmental pressure. Then the studies fell victim to the 1981 funding crisis which also caused Tornado production rates to be reduced and the Mirage 4000 to be virtually shelved.

That a home-grown French aircraft and a joint

Anglo-German project (which has since received Italian support too) should have emerged from those aborted discussions can come as no surprise to anyone. What is dismaying is the fact that the officials who will probably determine the future shape of the European industry should have been so willing to let two years of valuable time slide by.

There is no doubt that if the two existing design teams were given some assurance of survival and autonomy a Eurofighter could evolve from ACA and ACX. But if that does not happen, the chances of two independent but very similar projects succeeding are minute. Moreover, one team could suffer fatally unless it received obvious and substantial quantities of non-returnable government funding.

The key to a secure future for Europe's military aerospace industry now lies as much in the hands of governments as in those of the engineers who will design and build the aircraft. It is imperative that in the coming year or so the planners in high places wake up to what is expected of them, and to what is required of them. What is expected is that they put their weight behind keeping one of Europe's most valuable indus-

trial assets intact. What is required is that they ensure that the aircraft which can best defend Europe is produced. The military commanders claim that for this purpose they need a flexible and highly capable fleet of aircraft. But if they are to have their way, Eurofighter alone is not enough.

Tornado, the newer Mirages and Gripen will be in service at the same time as Eurofighter, but what of the uniquely vital qualities offered by the vertical/short take-off and landing (V/Stol) Harrier? A supersonic Harrier has been dreamed of for a long time, and difficult as this will be to achieve, when it comes it will rewrite the air power textbook. There must surely be European interest in a development of a type that already sets enviable close-support and air-combat standards, and yet which is close to being exported lock, stock and barrel to the US because of "not invented here" prejudice on mainland Europe.

If Europe is to have an aerospace industry that is something more than a copier of American trends, the challenge of V/Stol must be answered. The industry clearly has the capacity to do so, and an advanced V/Stol timed to enter service in the mid-1990s is the obvious stablemate for a 1990 Eurofighter. This is the

Left: **Britain, West Germany and Italy have combined forces to propose the ACA, which would benefit greatly from lessons learned on the tri-national Tornado programme.** (BAe)

Below: **France's advanced combat aircraft project, ACX, is very similar to ACA. It is due to make its first flight in 1986.** (Dassault-Breguet)

best way of achieving the joint objectives of assuring the European aerospace industry of sufficient business, and of providing a more effective and flexible fighting force. Furthermore, it would improve the chances of selling aircraft abroad, and avoid the risk of Europe's becoming a mere technological colony of the United States.

Above: **Britain has pioneered operational V/Stol with the highly successful Harrier, which is tasked with rapid-response close air-support duties in Western Europe. A replacement type will be needed from the mid-1990s.** (*BAe*)

Below: **This supersonic V/Stol configuration for use in the 1990s is one of several being studied by British Aerospace.** (*BAe*)

New aircraft of the year

Michael J. H. Taylor

Many new aircraft made their first flights during the twelve-month period from June 1982. *New aircraft of the year* covers the more important and interesting types in chronological order.

ICA IAR-825TP Triumf, IAR-831 Pelican and IAR-99 Soim (Romania)
Turboprop, piston and turbojet-powered tandem two-seat trainers
First flight (Triumf): June 12, 1982

Using some components of the earlier IAR-823, including the landing gear and similar but strengthened wings capable of carrying practice weapons, the new IAR-825TP Triumf was first displayed in public at the 1982 Farnborough Show. It is a tandem two-seat trainer powered by a 507kW (680shp) Pratt & Whitney Aircraft of Canada PT6A-15AG turboprop. Construction of the prototype began in September 1981. A photograph of this aircraft (YR-IGB) can be found in *Too many trainers?* (page 133).

Data: Triumf
Powerplant: As above
Wing span: 10.30m (33ft 9½in)
Length overall: 8.90m (29ft 2½in)
Weight empty: 1,100kg (2,425lb)
Max T-O weight (normal): 2,350kg (5,181lb)
Max level speed (aerobatic): 550km/hr (341mph)
Max rate of climb at S/L: 960m (3,150ft)/min
Service ceiling: 9,000m (29,525ft)
Range with max fuel, 30min reserves: 1,400km (870 miles)
g limits: +6/−3

IAR-831 Pelican and IAR-99 Soim
A new piston-engined tandem two-seat trainer from ICA is the IAR-831 Pelican, which was to be seen in prototype form (YR-IGA) at the Paris Show of 1983.

Power is provided by a 216kW (290hp) Avco Lycoming IO-540-G1D5 flat-six engine. The IAR-831 is similar to the Triumf, with identical wing span and length, but has a maximum weight (in the strike role) of 1,500kg (3,307lb) and a maximum speed of 320km/hr (199mph).

ICA has also produced a prototype basic and advanced jet trainer known as the IAR-99 Soim. Powered by a Rolls-Royce Viper 632-41 turbojet produced under licence in Romania and rated at 17.8kN (4,000lb st), it has four underwing stores pylons. Wing span is 9.35m (30ft 8in), length 10.88m (35ft 8½in), max T-O weight 5,476kg (12,072lb), and maximum level speed 865km/hr (537mph).

Ganzer Model 75 Gemini (USA)
Two-seat sporting aircraft
First flight: June 1982

David W. Ganzer has built a two-seat sporting aircraft named the Gemini. Of foam and glassfibre construction, it has foreplanes and rear-mounted main wings with winglets at each tip. Unlike other homebuilt air-

Ganzer Model 75 Gemini two-seat homebuilt sporting aircraft.

craft of similar general design, the Gemini is powered by two engines in a push-pull arrangement. Design of the Gemini began in August 1980 and construction of a prototype started in March of the following year.

Powerplant: Two 48.5kW (65hp) Volkswagen 2,000cc
  modified motorcar engines, one in the nose and one
  in the tail
Wing span: 8.41m (27ft 7¼in)
Length overall: 5.33m (17ft 6in)
Weight empty, operating: 535kg (1,180lb)
Max T-O weight: 862kg (1,900lb)
Max level speed: 298km/hr (185mph)
Max rate of climb at S/L: 275m (900ft)/min
Range with max fuel: 1,931km (1,200 miles)

Beechcraft Model 38P Lightning (USA)
Four/six-seat cabin monoplane
First flight: June 14, 1982

The Model 38P Lightning has an airframe based upon that of the pressurised Baron Model 58P. It differs from the Baron mainly in having a single, nose-mounted turboprop. Manufacture of the first two Model 38P production Lightnings started in early 1983.

Three versions will be produced: the Model 38P, powered by a Pratt & Whitney Aircraft of Canada PT6A-40 turboprop flat-rated at 410-485kW (550-650shp) and driving a Hartzell three-blade constant-speed propeller; Model 38P-1, with a Pratt & Whitney Aircraft of Canada PT6A-116 turboprop; and Model 38P-2, powered by a Garrett TPE331-9 turboprop.

Powerplant: As above
Wing span: 11.53m (37ft 10in)
Length overall: 9.12m (29ft 11in)
Weights: Not available
*Max cruising speed (Models 38P/38P-I, at 7,620m;
  25,000ft), estimated:* 508km/hr (316mph)
Max certification ceiling, estimated: 7,620m (25,000ft)
*Max range at max-range power, 45min reserves (Model
  38P), estimated:* 2,068km (1,285 miles)

PZL Mielec M-21 Dromader Mini (Poland)
Single-seat agricultural aircraft
First flight: June 18, 1982

The Dromader Mini is a reduced-capacity version of the M-18A Dromader agricultural aircraft, with a shorter wing span, a hopper capacity of 1.70m³ (60ft³), and a 447kW (600hp) PZL-3SR seven-cylinder radial engine.

Powerplant: As above
Wing span: 14.51m (47ft 7¼in)
Length overall: 9.48m (31ft 1¼in)
Payload: 900kg (1,984lb)
Max T-O weight: 3,300kg (7,275lb)
Max level speed: 230km/hr (143mph)
Working speed range: 155-180km/hr (96-112mph)
Range, without reserves: 700km (435 miles)

British Aerospace (Hawker Siddeley) Vulcan tanker (UK)
Flight-refuelling tanker
First flight: June 18, 1982

Discussion of the possible conversion of RAF Vulcan bombers to supplement the service's fleet of Victor tankers began on April 30, 1982, as a result of experience in the Falklands War. Go-ahead was authorised on May 4 and fifty days later the first Vulcan tanker was flown to RAF Waddington. Redesign of the hose drum unit by Flight Refuelling Ltd permitted it to be mounted inside the ECM bay at the tail, and three cylindrical fuel tanks were installed in the bomb bay. The drogue was housed in a metal-and-wood box under the tailcone. The first transfer of fuel from a Vulcan, to a Victor tanker and a Vulcan bomber, was conducted on June 23, 1982.

British Aerospace VC10 K2 (UK)
Flight-refuelling tanker
First flight: June 22, 1982

The British Government decided in 1978 to investigate the feasibility of converting ex-civil VC10s into flight-refuelling tankers for the RAF. After a design study nine aircraft were acquired for this purpose. Five of the nine were standard Model 1101s built for BOAC, and the others were Model 1154 Super VC10s formerly used by East African Airways. These aircraft are now known as K2s and K3s respectively. After the RAF's Victor tankers have been retired the VC10 C1 multi-mission transports will be similarly converted.

Powerplant: Four 97kN (21,800lb st) Rolls-Royce
  Conway Mk 550B turbofans, interchangeable with
  the Conway 301s installed in the VC10 C1
Accommodation: Flight crew of four. Limited rear-
  facing seating for airlift of essential ground personnel
  when tanker is deployed away from its home base;
  K2 seats 18, K3 17. Forward underfloor freight hold
  is unchanged and can carry spares or refuelling pods
  during ferry flights. Fuel for flight-refuelling opera-

tions is accommodated in five cylindrical tanks installed within the fuselage. These tanks and the aircraft's basic fuel system are interconnected, and it is possible to transfer all but the fuel needed for the tanker's mission, and to take on fuel through a nose-mounted probe

Wing span: 44.55m (146ft 2in)
Length overall (K2), excluding refuelling probe: 48.36m (158ft 8in)

Riley Turbine P-210 (USA)
Higher-powered conversion of Cessna Model 210 Pressurised Centurion
First flight: June 30, 1982

Development of the Turbine P-210 by Riley started in November 1981. This aircraft differs from the standard Centurion in having a 507kW (680shp) Pratt & Whitney Aircraft of Canada PT6A-112 turboprop flat-rated to 373kW (500shp) and driving a Hartzell four-blade, constant-speed, fully feathering, reversible-pitch Q-tip propeller with spinner. The conversion includes installation of a new glassfibre aerodynamic cowling with inertial separator and electric-induction air-lip de-icing, electric propeller de-icing, a Lear Siegler 28V/200A starter/generator, a 28V/50A standby generator, Gill 639T heavy-duty battery installation, fuel computer, a new engine instrument panel, a 24V electrical system to meet FAA requirements, and Fling wingtip fuel tanks with a combined capacity of 62.5lit (16.5 US gal).

Powerplant: As above
Wing span: 11.20m (36ft 9in)
Length overall: 9.25m (30ft 4in)
Cruising speed (provisional, at 7,010m; 23,000ft): 483km/hr (300mph)
Max rate of climb at S/L: 670m (2,200ft)/min
Range, with IFR reserves: 1,609km (1,000 miles)

General Dynamics F-16XL (USA)
Advanced version of the F-16
First flight: July 3, 1982

General Dynamics is developing as a private venture an advanced version of the F-16 fighter incorporating new aerodynamics and systems technologies. The USAF has leased to General Dynamics two F-16 airframes, a Pratt & Whitney F100-PW-200 turbofan engine and one new two-seat cockpit, allowing the company to build one single-seat and one two-seat F-16XL demonstrator aircraft.

The most obvious external change is the adoption of

F-16XL flying alongside the F-16/79 demonstrator with standard wings.

a highly swept cranked-arrow wing which has an area more than double that of the standard F-16 unit. Graphite polyimide composite skins provide the strength and rigidity essential for maximum wing performance. The fuselage is lengthened by 1.42m (4ft 8in), the extra volume being used to increase the internal fuel capacity by 82 per cent and to provide additional space for avionics and sensors.

By comparison with the standard aircraft the F-16XL can take off and land in only two-thirds of the distance, carry double the number of weapons on its 29 hardpoints, and offer up to 45 per cent greater combat radius on internal fuel only.

The first full-scale development aircraft was delivered to Fort Worth in March 1981, followed by the second a few months later. The single-seater first flew in July 1982 and the two-seater on October 29 that year. The latter is powered by a General Electric F101 DFE engine. Initial testing of the aircraft ended in the spring of 1983.

Powerplant: As above
Wing span: 10.43m (34ft 2¾in)
Wing area, gross: 61.59m² (663ft²)
Length overall: 16.51m (54ft 1¾in)
Max external stores load: 6,803kg (15,000lb)
Max T-O weight: 21,772kg (48,000lb)
Max level speed: Mach 2
Max range: more than 4,630km (2,875 miles)
Design g limit: +9

Harbin Y-11T (Turbo-Panda) (China)
Twin-turboprop Stol general-purpose transport
First flight: July 14, 1982

Studies aimed at improving the payload-range of the radial-engined Y-11 led to the installation of two Pratt & Whitney Aircraft of Canada PT6A-11 turboprop engines in the Y-11T1 development aircraft. One Y-11T1 was completed for structural and static testing and two for flight tests.

The Y-11T also has an enlarged airframe, the longer fuselage accommodating up to 17 passengers in commuter configuration. The slightly longer-span wings incorporate a new aerofoil section and additional fuel tanks. The two Y-11T1 development aircraft will be used for geological survey work. Production aircraft, designated Y-12 or Yun-12, are powered by 462kW (620shp) PT6A-27 turboprops.

Powerplant: As above
Accommodation: Up to 17 passengers in commuter configuration, or 14 parachutists, or up to 1,700kg (3,748lb) of cargo. Baggage compartments in nose and at rear of passenger cabin, for 80kg (176lb) and 220kg (485lb) respectively
Wing span: 17.24m (56ft 6½in)
Length overall: 14.86m (48ft 9in)
Basic weight empty: 2,800kg (6,173lb)
Max T-O weight: 4,700kg (10,362lb)
Max level speed (Y-11T2): 302km/hr (187mph)
Max rate of climb at S/L (Y-11T2): 480m (1,575ft)/min
Service ceiling (Y-11T1): 7,000m (22,965ft)
Range with 1,445kg (3,185lb) payload (17 passengers and baggage), 45min reserves: 410km (255 miles)
Range at 3,000m (9,845ft) with max fuel (Y-11T1), no reserves: 1,410km (876 miles)

Co Z Development Cozy (USA)
Side-by-side two-seat homebuilt sporting aircraft
First flight: July 19, 1982

The Cozy was conceived by Nathan D. Puffer as a side-by-side two-seat development of the Rutan Long-EZ. Construction of the prototype began in July 1981. Though the Cozy was intended originally to be a one-off, Puffer received a licence to market the aircraft from Rutan and established the Co Z Development Corporation for this purpose. Plans are now available to amateur constructors. A third person or baggage can be accommodated behind the two front seats.

Powerplant: One 88kW (118hp) Avco Lycoming O-235-L2C flat-four engine driving a two-blade pusher propeller
Wing span: 7.96m (26ft 1¼in)
Length overall: 5.12m (16ft 9½in)
Weight empty, basic: 386kg (850lb)
Max T-O weight: 680kg (1,500lb)
Max level speed at S/L: 306km/hr (190mph)
Max rate of climb at S/L: 457m (1,500ft)/min
Service ceiling: 6,100m (20,000ft)
Range with max fuel, 225km/hr (140mph), 3,600m (12,00ft), 1½hr reserves: 2,896km (1,800 miles)

British Aerospace 146 Series 200 (UK)
Four-turbofan short-range transport
First flight: August 1, 1982

First flight of BAe 146 Series 200 prototype G-WISC came eleven months after the debut of the Series 100 prototype. Compared with the Series 100, the Series

Left: Co Z Development Cozy, a side-by-side two-seat development of the RAF Long-EZ.

200 is suitable for operation from paved runways only, has increased seating for between 82 and 109 passengers in a lengthened fuselage (a mixed passenger/freight version is planned), and maximum take-off weight, underfloor cargo volume and range are increased.

Powerplant: Four 31.0kN (6,970lb st) Avco Lycoming ALF 502R-5 turbofans
Accommodation: As above
Wing span: 26.34m (86ft 5 in)
Length overall: 28.55m (93ft 8in)
Typical operating weight empty: 22,135kg (48,800lb)
Max payload: 10,206kg (22,500lb)
Max T-O weight: 40,597kg (89,500lb)
Max cruising speed at 7,925m (26,000ft): 778km/hr (483mph)
Range with max payload, with allowances: 1,853km (1,150 miles)

Hawk GafHawk 125 (USA)
Turboprop-powered freighter
First flight: August 19, 1982

Hawk Industries specialises in equipment for oil and water well-drilling and fencing. Having experienced difficulties in transporting its products, in 1977 the company initiated design of a freight-carrying aircraft that would be both faster than road transport, and cheaper and easier to load and unload than conventional aicraft.

The resulting aircraft became known as the GafHawk (signifying General Aviation Freighter) and is now managed by the company's aircraft division. Although the following data refer to the prototype, the division has also projected larger and smaller derivatives. Many GafHawks have since been ordered.

Features of the GafHawk include Stol capability for operation into and out of small, unprepared strips, a single turboprop engine for economic operation, a square-section fuselage for maximum utilisation of internal capacity, under-tail loading at truckbed height, ease of certification, and single-pilot operation. Before the prototype was built the concept was flight-tested using an extensively rebuilt Piper Tri-Pacer known as the MiniHawk.

Powerplant: One 875kW (1,173shp) Pratt & Whitney Aircraft of Canada PT6A-45R turboprop
Accommodation: Freight up to 6.1m (20ft) in length with rear loading door closed
Wing span: 21.79m (71ft 6in)
Length overall: 14.30m (46ft 11in)
Max T-O weight: 6,350kg (14,000lb)
Max cruising speed at 3,050m (10,000ft), estimated: 282km/hr (175mph)
Max rate of climb at S/L, estimated: 290m (950ft)/min
Service ceiling, estimated: 5,485m (18,000ft)
Range with max fuel, estimated: 1,668km (1,036 miles)

Hawk Industries GafHawk 125 turboprop-powered freighter.

Seawind International Seawind (Canada)
Four-seat amphibian
First flight: August 23, 1982

Seawind International, a division of Rodlen Aircraft Incorporated, was formed to develop and market in kit form a four-seat amphibian known as the Seawind. Most parts are made of fibre-reinforced plastics (FRP) and kits include some finished sub-assemblies.

The prototype Seawind has been flight-tested against the performance requirements of FAR Part 23 and is said to have exceeded the minima by a substantial margin. By early 1983 about 40 Seawinds had been ordered by amateur constructors. The prototype was still undergoing development at that point and it was expected that some changes could still be introduced before kits became available.

The Seawind has cantilever shoulder-mounted wings, a rakish fuselage with a single-step hull, a sweptback fin and rudder, and an all-moving one-piece tailplane, and is powered by a 224kW (300hp) Avco Lycoming IO-360-C1C flat-four engine mounted midway up and ahead of the fin.

Powerplant: As above
Wing span: 10.16m (33ft 4in)
Length overall: 8.53m (28ft 0in)
Weight empty: 748kg (1,650lb)
Max T-O weight: 1,156kg (2,550lb)
Cruising speed (75% power): 274km/hr (170mph)
Max rate of climb at S/L: 290m (950ft)/min
Range: 1,046km (650 miles)

Northrop F-20 Tigershark (USA)
Single-seat light tactical fighter
First flight: August 30, 1982

Formerly known as the F-5G Tigershark, the F-20 is the latest development of the successful F-5 series of lightweight tactical aircraft. It was conceived as an export fighter powered by a single 75.6kN (17,000lb st) General Electric F404-GE-100 afterburning turbofan instead of the previously standard pair of General Electric J85 turbojets. With empty weight increased by 15 per cent and the F404 yielding 70 per cent more thrust, the F-20 offers significant performance improvements over its predecessors. The first nation to express interest in the Tigershark was Bahrain.

Powerplant: As above
Armament: Two M39 20mm cannon plus more than 3,630kg (8,000lb) of external weapons
Wing span, with missiles at wingtips: 8.53m (27ft 11⅞in)
Length overall, excluding probe: 14.17m (46 ft 6in)
Weight empty: 5,089kg (11,220lb)

Seen here showing off its high-performance abilities with a vertical climb, the Northrop F-20 Tigershark can accelerate from Mach 0.3 to Mach 0.9 in 28sec at 3,050m (10,000ft). (*Northrop*)

Max T-O weight: 11,925kg (26,290lb)
Max level speed at height: Mach 2
Max rate of climb at S/L, estimated: 16,095m (52,800ft)/min
Service ceiling, estimated: 16,765m (55,000ft)
Combat radius with max internal fuel and two 1,041lit (275 US gal) external tanks, two Sidewinder missiles, seven Mk 82 bombs, 5min combat at S/L military power, 20min fuel reserves at S/L, hi-lo-hi mission: 713km (443 miles)
g limit: +9

Beechcraft 1900 Airliner (USA)
Twin-turboprop commuter airliner
First flight: September 3, 1982

Work on this new pressurised 19-passenger commuter airliner started in 1979, and construction of prototypes for performance, system and instrument testing began in 1981. FAA certification was due to be gained in late 1983.

The 1900 Airliner is a low-wing aircraft with a pressurised fuselage having the same cross-section as that of the Super King Air. Power is provided by two 745kW (1,000shp) Pratt & Whitney Aircraft of Canada PT6A-65B turboprops. A T tail is fitted. An optional cargo door can replace the standard rear passenger door, which supplements the forward door with airstair. Airliners are being constructed on a new production line at Wichita.

Powerplant: As above
Accommodation: Standard seating for 19 passengers
Wing span: 16.61m (54ft 5¾in)
Length overall: 17.63m (57ft 10in)
Max payload: 1,814kg (4,000lb)
Max T-O weight: 6,915kg (15,245lb)
Max cruising speed at 6,350kg (14,000lb), 3,050m (10,000ft): 491km/hr (305mph)
Range with max fuel and max payload, at 7,620m (25,000ft), with reserves: 1,727km (1,073 miles)

Mudry CAP X and CAP X Super (France)
Two-seat basic flying trainers
First flights: September 10, 1982, and May 4, 1983, respectively

In 1981 Avions Mudry announced the development of a new side-by-side two-seat low-cost training aircraft, to be powered by the company's new Mudry-Buchoux M-4-80 flat-four engine (59kW; 80hp). Designed for low initial cost, minimum maintenance requirements and low fuel consumption, the prototype (F-WZCJ), constructed partly from composite materials, appeared partially completed at the 1981 Paris Show. It flew for the first time in September of the following year.

Because the M-4-80 engine is still under development, the company is marketing the same airframe, fitted with an 80kW (108hp) Avco Lycoming engine, as the CAP X Super trainer, which first flew in May 1983 and was exhibited at the 1983 Paris Show. By mid-May 1983 the CAP X Super had completed ten flying hours in the hands of nine different pilots.

Data: Mudry CAP X, with estimated performance figures
Powerplant: As above
Wing span: 8.00m (26ft 3in)
Length overall: 5.90m (19ft 4½in)
Weight empty: 340kg (750lb)
Max T-O weight: 530kg (1,168lb)
Max cruising speed at 1,500m (4,920ft): 189km/hr (117mph)
Range with max fuel: 740km (460 miles)
g limits: +4.4/−1.8

Mudry CAP X Super seen at the 1983 Paris Show.
(*Austin J. Brown*)

HAL Ajeet Trainer (India)
Tandem two-seat operational trainer
First flight: September 20, 1982

The Ajeet Trainer is a two-seat version of the Ajeet, retaining the four underwing hardpoints and full combat capability of the single-seater. Two of the fuselage fuel tanks were deleted to make room for the second cockpit, although this can be offset by replacing the Aden cannon with internal fuel. The aircraft's fighting capability can then be restored by carrying a 7.62mm gun pod on each of the inboard wing pylons. Instructor and pupil are seated on Martin-Baker ejection seats.

Powerplant: One 21.57kN (4,850lb st) Rolls-Royce Orpheus 701-01AT non-afterburning turbojet
Armament: Two Aden Mk 4 30mm cannon in air-intake fairings. Each inboard underwing pylon is capable of carrying a Type 122 practice rocket pod, one pod of 57mm rockets, one cluster bomb or one CBLS with four 25lb practice bombs. A 250kg bomb can be carried on each inboard pylon, with a 136.5lit (30 Imp gal) drop-tank on each outboard pylon.

Wing span: 6.73m (22ft 1in)
Length overall: 10.45m (34ft 3½in)
Basic weight empty, including crew: 2,940kg (6,482lb)
Max external stores load: 850kg (1,874lb)
Max T-O weight: 4,536kg (10,000lb)
Max level speed at S/L: 1,070km/hr (665mph)
Max rate of climb at S/L: 3,240m (10,625ft)/min
Service ceiling: 14,000m (45,925ft)
Range with max internal fuel, 135lit (29.7 Imp gal) reserves: 900km (559 miles)

Fishercraft Zippy Sport (USA)
Single-seat homebuilt cabin lightplane
First flight: October 9, 1982

Fishercraft Incorporated is marketing plans for a new single-seat strut-braced high-wing monoplane known as the Zippy Sport. Design of this aircraft began in the spring of 1979 and construction of the prototype started in the following summer. It received FAA certification in the Unlimited Experimental category in January 1983. By then a second prototype was under construction, and was subsequently followed by a third. The second and third aircraft were built to the plans which are now available to homebuilders.

Powerplant: One 22.4kW (30hp) Cuyuna 430RR two-stroke engine
Wing span: 8.03m (26ft 4in)
Length overall: 5.44m (17ft 10in)
Weight empty: 156.5kg (345lb)
Max T-O weight: 272kg (600lb)
Max level speed at 305m (1,000ft): 161km/hr (100mph)
Max rate of climb at S/L: 229m (750ft)/min
Range with 1.9lit (0.5 US gal) reserves: 322km (200 miles)

Hughes Model 530F (USA)
Light helicopter
First flight: October 22, 1982

First announced at the Helicopter Association International meeting at Las Vegas, Nevada, in early 1982, the Model 530F derives from the Model 500D and is intended for operation at high altitudes or in high temperatures. It has the new fuselage of the Model 500E and a 485kW (650shp) Allison 250-C30 turboshaft which fits into an engine compartment identical with that of the 250-C20B. The main rotor has a 0.3m (1ft) increase in diameter, giving additional lift capability, and the diameter of the tail rotor is increased by 5cm (2in). The tailboom is extended to accommodate the larger main rotor disc. A cargo hook capable of lifting an external load of up to 907kg (2,000lb) will be made available.

Fishercraft Zippy Sport, a single-seat homebuilt cabin lightplane.

Powerplant: As above
Main-rotor diameter: 8.36m (27ft 5in)
Length of fuselage: 7.25m (23ft 9½in)
Weight empty: 705kg (1,555lb)
Max normal T-O weight: 1,406kg (3,100lb)
Max cruising speed from S/L to 1,525m (5,000ft): 250km/hr (155mph)
Max rate of climb at S/L: 543m (1,780ft)/min
Service ceiling: 5,335m (17,500ft)
Range, 2min warm-up, standard fuel, no reserves, at 1,525m (5,000ft): 434km (269 miles)

Above: **Latest variant of the Hughes Model 500 series is the Model 530F.**

Below: **Seen here on the point of making its first flight is the Slingsby T67M Firefly two-seat basic trainer.**

Slingsby T67M Firefly 160 (UK)
Two-seat military basic trainer
First flight: December 5, 1982

This military basic trainer version of the T67 is based on the glass-reinforced plastic T67B. Power is provided by a 119kW (160hp) Avco Lycoming AEIO-320-D1B flat-four engine. Blind-flying instrumentation is standard. Production deliveries started in 1983.

Powerplant: As above
Wing span: 10.59m (34ft 9in)
Length overall: 7.01m (23ft 0in)
Weight empty, basic: 640kg (1,410lb)
Max T-O weight: 907kg (2,000lb)
Max level speed: 256km/hr (159mph)
Max rate of climb at S/L: 360m (1,180ft)/min
Service ceiling: 4,570m (15,000ft)
Range with max fuel at 75% power, with allowances: 676km (420 miles)
g limits: +6/−3 at 884kg (1,950lb) AUW

Cessna Caravan (USA)
Utility aircraft
First flight: December 9, 1982

Cessna claims that the Caravan is the first all-new single-engined turboprop general-aviation aircraft. It is intended to supplement or replace the large number of de Havilland Canada Beavers and Otters and Cessna 180s, 185s and 206s now operated throughout the world. The engineering prototype, which first flew in December 1982, looks very different from earlier Cessnas.

The Caravan will be capable of high performance with a heavy load, of getting into and out of unprepared airstrips, and of economical operation and reliability with minimum maintenance. Options will include weather radar, air-conditioning, oxygen systems and, probably, role packages for aerial firefighting, photographic, agricultural spraying, ambulance, border patrol, parachutist and supply-dropping, surveillance and other duties. The aircraft will be offered with wheel, float or ski landing gears.

Powerplant: One 447kW (600shp) Pratt & Whitney Aircraft of Canada PT6A-114 turboprop
Accommodation: Pilot and up to 14 passengers, cargo, etc
Wing span: 15.75m (51ft 8in)
Length overall: 11.46m (37ft 7in)
Max useful load: 1,361kg (3,000lb)
Max T-O weight, landplane: 3,039kg (6,700lb)
Max cruising speed, landplane: 344km/hr (214mph)
Max rate of climb at S/L, landplane: more than 457m (1,500ft)/min
Range with max fuel, landplane: more than 1,854km (1,152 miles)

IAC TA16 Seafire (USA)
Four-seat light amphibian
First flight: December 10, 1982

International Aeromarine Corporation was formed to develop and certificate the TA16 Seafire, the latest light amphibian from David B. Thurston. Designed as a production version of the TA16 Trojan, an amphibian intended for construction by amateur builders, the Seafire meets the requirements of FAR Pt 23, Amendment 24.

Powerplant: One 186kW (250hp) Avco Lycoming O-540-A4D5 flat-six engine mounted on a pylon over the wing
Wing span: 11.28m (37ft 0in)
Length overall: 8.28m (27ft 2in)
Weight empty, equipped: 862kg (1,900lb)

Max T-O weight: 1,360kg (3,000lb)
Max level speed at 2,135m (7,000ft): 265km/hr (164mph)
Max rate of climb at S/L: 323m (1,060ft)/min
Service ceiling: 5,485m (18,000ft)
Range with max fuel: 1,528km (950 miles)

Dassault-Breguet Mirage IIING (France)
Single-seat combat aircraft
First flight: December 21, 1982

The new-generation (*Nouvelle-Génération*) version of the Mirage III incorporates two major innovations: foreplanes and a fly-by-wire control system. The prototype took off for the first time in December 1982 and subsequently appeared at the 1983 Paris Show. Compared with the standard Mirage III, the IIING is expected to demonstrate improved manoeuvrability, handling, and take-off and landing performance.

Powered by a Snecma Atar 9K-50 afterburning turbojet and fitted with a completely modernised weapon system, the Mirage IIING is intended as an export fighter to be produced in parallel with the Mirage F.1 and Mirage 2000.

Shorts Sherpa (UK)
Civil freighter
First flight: December 23, 1982

The Sherpa is a civil freighter version of the Shorts 330-200, from which it differs mainly in having a Skyvan-type full-width rear loading door. It retains the powerplant and forward freight door of the 330-200 and can carry a 3,175kg (7,000lb) cargo load or a typical 2,268kg (5,000lb) payload over a range of 1,239km (770 miles).

Powerplant: Two 893kW (1,198shp) Pratt & Whitney Aircraft of Canada PT6A-45R turboprops
Wing span: 22.76m (74ft 8in)
Length overall: 17.69m (58ft 0½in)

Saab-Fairchild 340 (Sweden/USA)
Twin-turboprop transport
First flight January 25, 1983

In January 1980 Saab-Scania of Sweden and Fairchild Industries of the USA announced that they were to develop, produce and market a new transport aircraft. The resulting Saab-Fairchild 340 is the first collaborative venture of its kind between members of the Euro-

The Shorts Sherpa, featuring a full-width rear loading door, is the civil freight version of the Shorts 330-200.

pean and US aerospace industries. Fairchild is responsible for marketing the aircraft in the USA, Canada and Mexico, and Saab-Fairchild MB for sales in all other parts of the world.

Design of the Saab-Fairchild 340 emphasises simplicity of systems, operation and maintenance, with quick turnrounds made possible by a number of built-in features which will make the aircraft independent of ground handling equipment. It will operate particularly on short-haul, low-density routes and is available in both airliner and corporate transport versions.

Initial deliveries are expected to begin in the spring of 1984. By the spring of 1983 orders and options totalled more than 100, of which about half were from US customers. It is expected that production will total 24 aircraft during 1984, rising thereafter to a peak of 72 in 1987.

Powerplant: Two 1,215kW (1,630shp) General Electric CT7-5A turboprops in airliner version. Two 1,193kW (1,600shp) CT7-7Es in corporate version
Accommodation: Up to 34 passengers or mixed passenger/cargo. Corporate/executive version seats 16 passengers
Wing span: 21.44m (70ft 4in)
Length overall: 19.71m (64ft 8in)
Typical operating weight empty: 7,194kg (15,860lb)
Max T-O weight: 11,793kg (26,000lb)

Max cruising speed at 4,570m (15,000ft), AUW of 11,204kg (24,700lb): 508km/hr (315mph)
Max rate of climb at S/L: 549m (1,800ft)/min
Service ceiling: 7,620m (25,000ft)
Range, allowances for 185km (115-mile) diversion and 45min hold, with max passenger payload: 1,686km (1,048 miles)

Dassault-Breguet Mirage 2000N (France)
Two-seat strike aircraft
First flight: February 3, 1983

The first of two prototype Mirage 2000N strike aircraft made its first flight in February 1983. A two-seat low-altitude penetration version of the Mirage 2000, it is stressed for flight at a typical 1,110km/hr (690mph) at 60m (200ft) above the ground. It is equipped with ESD Antilope V terrain-following radar, two Sagem inertial platforms, improved TRT AHV12 radio-altimeter, Thomson-CSF colour CRT, an Omera vertical camera, and special ECM. Production deliveries to the French Air Force, with which it will supersede the Mirage IVA nuclear strike aircraft, are scheduled to begin in 1986. The first export customers for the Mirage 2000N, in non-nuclear-armed form, are Egypt and India. Most of the Indian aircraft will eventually be assembled under licence in that country.

Armament: French aircraft will have provision for ASMP nuclear missiles

Piper Cheyenne IV (USA)
Light business aircraft
First flight: February 23, 1983

This new business aircraft combines the basic airframe, components and systems of the Cheyenne III with two new 746kW (1,000shp) Garrett TPE331-14A/14B turboprops, an updated electrical system and other changes. The prototype first flew in February 1983 and production deliveries are due to begin in May 1984.

Powerplant: As above
Accommodation: Two crew and six passengers
Wing span over tip-tanks: 14.53m (47ft 8in)
Length overall: 12.23m (43ft 4¾in)
Weight empty, standard: 3,198kg (7,050lb)
Max T-O weight: 5,420kg (11,950lb)
Cruising speed, max cruise power at AUW of 4,762kg (10,500lb), 6,860m (22,500ft): 650km/hr (404mph)
Max rate of climb at S/L: 1,036m (3,400ft)/min
Service ceiling: more than 12,500m (41,000ft)
Max range, max-range power at 11,900m (39,000ft), with allowances: 2,592km (1,611 miles)

Piper Cheyenne IV makes its first flight at Lakeland, Florida. (*Piper*)

Stolp Super Starduster (USA)
Single-seat aerobatic biplane
First flight: April 1, 1983

The Super Starduster is the first of a new series of special aerobatic aircraft from Stolp, which supplies plans, kits and materials for several aircraft to amateur constructors. Design work started in May 1981 and certification was gained in May 1983. The aircraft features a unique linkage between the ailerons and flaps, allowing the former to serve as flaps (in the down position) in normal flight or as additional manoeuvring surfaces (in the up position) for outside loops during inverted flight.

Stolp Super Starduster, commissioned by aerobatic pilot Dick Green. (*Don Dwiggins*)

Powerplant: One 149kW (200hp) Avco Lycoming IO-360-A1A flat-four engine
Wing span: 5.94m (19ft 6in)
Length overall: 4.88m (16ft 0in)
Weight empty, basic operating: 426kg (940lb)
Max T-O weight: 680kg (1,500lb)
Max level speed at 2,440m (8,000ft): 289km/hr (180mph)
Max rate of climb at S/L: 914m (3,000ft)/min
Service ceiling: 3,810m (12,500ft)
Range with max fuel: 816km (507 miles)

Piper (PA-48) Enforcer (USA)
Single-seat turboprop-powered attack aircraft
First flight: April 9, 1983

Having acquired from Cavalier Aircraft Corporation the original programme for a modern version of the North American P-51 Mustang, Piper announced in September 1981 the receipt of a USAF contract covering the design, development and testing of two prototype Enforcer lightweight close-support aircraft. Piper has introduced significant changes to the original Enforcer, first flown during 1970-71, including aerodynamic improvements to the tailplane, modifications to the aileron control system, and provision for weapons.

The Enforcer is to be evaluated primarily as a close

Piper Enforcer, a modern ground-attack development of the North American P-51 Mustang.

air-support type, but also meets the basic counter-insurgency requirement. A tandem two-seat dual-control trainer version with combat capability is projected.

Powerplant: One 1,823ekW (2,445ehp) Avco Lycoming T55-L-9 turboprop
Armament: External weapons only, carried on six underwing pylons. Max permissible load 2,576kg (5,680lb), including gun pods, rockets and bombs
Wing span over tip-tanks: 12.60m (41ft 4in)
Length overall: 10.41m (34ft 2in)
Weight empty: about 3,266kg (7,200lb)
Max T-O weight: 6,350kg (14,000lb)
Max level speed at 4,575m (15,000ft): 556km/hr (345mph)
Max rate of climb at S/L: 762m (2,500ft)/min
Service ceiling: 6,100m (20,000ft)
Combat radius with two 30mm gun pods: 740km (460 miles)

Mooney M-30 Model 301 (USA)
Six-seat pressurised cabin monoplane
First flight: April 21, 1983

Announced at the 1980 Reading Show, the cantilever low-wing M-30 features an all-metal two-spar wing with Eppler advanced aerodynamic section, two top-surface spoilers on each wing to supplement roll control, and Fowler-type trailing-edge flaps over 70 per cent of the span. Power is supplied by a 261kW (350hp) Avco Lycoming TIO-540 turbocharged engine and equipment includes anti-icing gear, weather radar and

advanced avionics for communications and navigation. Production aircraft are expected to be available in 1985.

Powerplant: As above
Wing span: 11.28m (37ft 0in)
Weight empty: 1,043kg (2,300lb)
Max T-O weight: 1,769kg (3,900lb)
Max level speed at 7,620m (25,000ft): 485km/hr (301mph)
Max rate of climb at S/L: 420m (1,380ft)/min
Service ceiling: 7,620m (25,000ft)
Range (75% power) at 7,620m (25,000ft): 1,800km (1,118 miles)

Dornier Do 24TT (West Germany)
All-weather amphibian flying boat
First flight: April 25, 1983

Convinced of the need for an all-weather amphibian flying boat to perform maritime surveillance and air-sea rescue duties in the manner of the Grumman HU-16 Albatross, Dornier has produced the Do 24TT, based on the Second World War Do 24T ocean-going flying boat but with many important new features. The Do 24TT demonstrator flew for the first time in April 1983. It was to be tested over a period of 14 to 16 months to study the effects of the new technologies on the seaworthiness, operational flexibility, performance and economy of an advanced amphibious flying boat. It is powered by three 839 kW (1,125shp) Pratt & Whitney Aircraft of Canada PT6A turboprops, each mounted in a streamlined nacelle at the leading edge of the wing. This has a rectangular planform to the beginning of the wingtips, and a Do A-5 low-drag, high-lift aerofoil section throughout. The wing's triangular tips produce a reduction in induced drag by comparison with conventional wingtips. The Do 24TT's retractable landing gear comprises Do 31 twin-wheel main units plus a new single-wheel nose unit.

Powerplant: As above
Wing span: 30.00m (98ft 5in)
Length overall: 21.95m (72ft 0¼in)
Max T-O weight, from land: 14,000kg (30,865lb)
Max T-O weight, from water: 12,000kg (26,455lb)

British Aerospace BAe 125 Series 800 (UK)
Twin-turbofan business transport aircraft
First flight: May 26, 1983

Powerplant: Two 19.13kN (4,300lb st) Garrett TFE731-5R-1H turbofans
Wing span: 15.66m (51ft 4½in)
Length overall: 15.60m (51ft 2in)
Basic weight: 6,676kg (14,720lb)
Max T-O weight: 12,430kg (27,400lb)
Max level speed and max cruising speed at 8,840m (29,000ft): 858km/hr (533mph)
Service ceiling: 13,110m (43,000ft)
Range with max fuel: 5,680km (3,530 miles)

This latest and most advanced version of the BAe 125 is primarily a business aircraft but can be used in a wide variety of other civil and military roles. The Series 800A is the version for the North American market and the Series 800B is intended for sale elsewhere. Many airframe improvements have been incorporated into the Series 800, including an increase in wing span to reduce induced drag, improve aerodynamic efficiency and accommodate additional fuel. The aircraft's interior has also been redesigned. There is seating for up to 14 passengers.

Latest version of the BAe 125 is the Series 800. (*BAe*)

Flat-out with America's air racers

Don Berliner

The majestic Sierra Nevada Mountains form a solemn backdrop to the flamboyant Reno Air Races, where brilliantly decorated Mustangs, Bearcats, Sea Furies and Corsairs fly 30m (100ft) above the sagebrush, their engines screaming louder than any should. Steep banks around checkered pylons, the ex-fighters wingtip-to-wingtip at close to 725km/hr (450mph), and 40,000 people on their feet, waving their arms and cheering their favourites on to victory: this is US air racing at its best.

For almost 20 years Stead Airport — located on a plateau in the midst of thoroughly inhospitable desert just a few miles from Reno's insatiable slot machines — has been the heart and soul of American air racing. It was here that the National Air Races were recreated in 1964 by cattle rancher/hydroplane racer Bill Stead so that he could have a place to race his personal Bearcat. Since that first event the Unlimited Class (so named because of the power and cost of the aeroplanes) has been in the spotlight, achieving higher speeds and making far more noise than other type of racing, anywhere. That first year the big race, around an eight-mile lopsided course, was won by a well maintained Mustang with a strong engine but few modifications at a speed of 590km/hr (367mph). In 1982 the winner was another Mustang, but this time modified from spinner to tailcone and packing double the original power. It won at 650km/hr (405mph), having qualified at more than 708km/hr (440mph).

Given enough motivation and money, there does not appear to be any speed limit in sight for Reno's souped-up ex-fighters. A Rolls-Royce Griffon-powered P-51D Mustang, now sadly but a memory, holds the world speed record for piston-engined aeroplanes at 803.138km/hr (499.047mph), and faster models are in the works. Right behind them, though with several years' development to go, are the first of a new generation of custom-built Unlimiteds, direct descendants of the spine-chilling Gee Bee, Wedell Williams and Laird racers that inspired a generation back in the 1930s.

Sharing Reno's spacious ramp each year, in the shadow of the mighty Unlimiteds, are the Formula One racers. For their size and power these are among the most efficient flying machines yet created. This most durable of all racing classes got started in the late 1940s, when all a pilot had to do to win was fly at 282km/hr (175mph). At Reno in 1982 the top 16 qualifiers exceeded 322km/hr (200mph), and the best of them lapped the 5km, six-pylon oval course at more than 370km/hr (230mph) — all on the estimated 100.5kW (135hp) of a basically stock Continental O-200 engine.

Mixed in with the Formula Ones were the Sport and Racing Biplanes, happy reminders of air racing's past. These machines, many of them flown regularly for sport, race just as close to the pylons and to each other as do their more pure-bred companions. And some, such as the exceptionally streamlined, tandem-winged Amsoil-Rutan Racer of Dan Mortensen, are heralding a new era in biplane competition.

The fifth class at Reno is for stock-looking North American trainers of Second World War vintage known variously as AT-6s, SNJs, Texans and Harvards. Thanks to meticulous clean-ups and higher than normal power settings, they are capable of astonishing speeds. Ralph Twombly's qualifying lap around the new 8km (5-mile) course, at 352.85km/hr (219.25mph), suggests a level speed of at least 386km/hr (240mph)!

After three days of qualifying and practice, racing began in earnest on Friday September 17 with eight elimination races and continued on Saturday with seven more, interspersed with airshow acts. With almost $250,000 in prizes on the line, competition for places in the championship heats was fierce. When the leading aeroplanes in some early heats crossed the finish line after six laps of the most gruelling flying, they had won by margins of less than one second.

Finally, on the Sunday, all was set for the championships in the five classes. The crowd, of at least 35,000, was spilling out of the bleachers. The weather, which had been cold, windy and wet for most of the week, was little better, but there were no worries about safety and so the programme proceeded on schedule.

First off were the Sport Biplanes, eight of which were led across the finish line after six laps of the 5km course by Don Fairbanks in a Knight Twister at

Above: **Pat Hines' Willians-Cangie** *Sundancer* **Racing Biplane, an all-metal aeroplane that began as a Midget Mustang and was then highly modified with new wings and a 119kW (160hp) Avco Lycoming engine.** (*Adelbert F. Chute*)

277.95km/hr (172.71mph). Second came Bob Hugo at 276.34km/hr (171.71mph) in *Bit of Honey*, and Dave Morss was third with 275.70km/hr (171.31mph). Barely three seconds separated these three.

Next came the Racing Biplanes, with the closest race of the year. Right at the finish Pat Hines in *Sundancer* nipped past Dan Mortensen flying the Amsoil-Rutan. Their speeds were 337.00km/hr (209.40mph) and 336.69km/hr (209.21mph) respectively, a margin of victory of 0.3sec or about 27m (90ft)!

The Formula One Championship, on the same course, was almost as close, with Jon Sharp beating Phil Fogg (both in modified Cassutt Racers). Their speeds were 361.33km/hr (224.52mph) and 360.33km/hr (223.90mph) respectively. In third place was young John "Dusty" Dowd, nephew of the late Bill Falck, one of America's all-time great air racers. But eliminated in a heat was a crowd favourite, rookie racer/veteran astronaut Deke Slayton.

The AT-6 race, usually very close because of the great similarity of the Pratt & Whitney-powered trainers, was a breeze for top qualifier Twombly. He led his nearest rival by more than a mile at the finish, winning at 363.2km/hr (225.68mph).

Thus the stage was set for the Unlimited Championship race, the one that most of the spectators had come to Reno to see. Six Mustangs and the new F2G Corsair (an ex-US Navy machine that had just received a huge Pratt & Whitney R-4360 engine developing close to 2,983kW; 4,000hp) were led toward the starting line in full flight by Bob Hoover in his P-51D pace aircraft. When their formation was to his liking, he released them and quickly climbed out of the way.

The sound of 30,000 horsepower echoed off the mountains as the finely tuned racers streaked low, almost vanishing on the far side of the 14.8km course. The battle was clearly between Ron Hevle, who qualified at 709km/hr (440.6mph) in Mustang *Dago Red*, and John Crocker in Mustang *Sumthin' Else* at 699km/hr (434.3mph). They poured it on, hoping that their highly modified Rolls-Royce Merlins would hold together for the 11min required to fly eight laps of the big race. But at manifold pressures of at least 100lb/in² there is just so much that even the finest of engines can endure, and on Lap 4 Crocker's surrendered to the inevitable and blew up. Hevle, in his first major race, cruised on to victory at an average speed of "just"

Below: **Some of the Mustang and Corsair Unlimiteds and the Rockwell International-sponsored pace-plane, flown by Bob Hoover, in the pit area at Reno.** (*Adelbert F. Chute*)

Above: **Awaiting the starter's flag is Jon Sharp in his modified Cassutt Racer** *Aero Magic.* (*Adelbert F. Chute*)

Right: **Veteran AT-6 racer John Mosby banks into a pylon turn in his AT-6G, which has been a top performer for more than ten years.** (*Adelbert F. Chute*)

651.9km/hr (405.1mph). More than three miles back were Clay Klabo and Del Williams, a half second apart at 621km/hr (386mph). In fourth was Steve Hinton, with 583km/hr (362.5mph) on the still-new F2G's first outing in an Unlimited final.

Despite more rain, cold and wind than is usual at Reno, the fans ate it up, most of them having made plans to return even before this year's race had begun. It is a tradition with those who live for speed, because nowhere else in the world can one be certain of seeing the Unlimiteds. The Formula Ones, Biplanes and AT-6s are a fine spectacle, but Reno means Unlimited. And, to a great extent, Reno means American air racing, since it contributes about 90 per cent of any season's total prize money. It is also so well established that the other races seem to be little more than supporting acts. But there are other races, and there are indications that the sport may be re-awakening in the eastern part of the country.

There was a race at Petersburg, Virginia, that drew enough response to warrant at least one more try. The Formula One competition was won by Jimmy Miller in his fibreglass pusher *Texas Gem* at 359km/hr (223mph), followed by Chuck Andrews at 344km/hr (214mph) in Paul Musso's *Real Sporty*. The sole American Formula Vee race of the year was a close battle between Richard Reichelt in E. C. Fisher's *Blueberry* and Charlie Terry in his own *Beetle Bomb*, with the former winning by 0.1sec with 214.05km/hr (133.01mph) to Terry's 213.98km/hr (132.96mph).

A new form of racing which is catching on in America is the speed/fuel-efficiency competition, the goal of which is the creation of more efficient light aircraft rather than thrills for the crowd. The oldest of these events is the Lowers-Baker-Falck 500, run during the Experimental Aircraft Association's giant Fly-in at Oshkosh in Wisconsin. This covers six laps of a cross-country course. The winner in 1982, as in 1981, was A. J. Smith in his purpose-built AJ-2, powered by a 156.5kW (210hp) Avco Lycoming engine. He averaged 359km/hr (223mph) for the 500 miles and used a mere 68lit (18 US gal) of fuel, for a consumption of 11.7km/lit (27½miles/US gal).

The major long-course event was the CAFE 400, held in northern California. This attracted 49 entries, from single-seat homebuilts to light twins. The scoring

Three Unlimiteds, two Mustangs and the clipped-wing Corsair, round a pylon during a preliminary heat. (Adelbert F. Chute)

Right: **Ron Hevle winning the Unlimited Class in the highly modified P-51D Mustang** *Dago Red.* **It was his first major race.** (Adelbert F. Chute)

Far right: **Ron Hevle's beautifully finished** *Dago Red*, **winner of the Unlimited Class. Racing modifications include a tiny canopy faired into new dorsal decking, clipped wings with Hoerner tips, and a highly tuned Merlin engine.** (Adelbert F. Chute)

system combines speed, fuel consumption and payload, and the race was won by Mooney chief engineer Roy Lopresti in a Mark 201. Second was Dick Rutan in a Long-EZ, and third was his brother Burt in the twin-engined Defiant.

A new event on the schedule was the Dulles 400, much like the CAFE race and conducted at Dulles International Airport, near Washington DC. This first, somewhat hesitant effort was plagued by bad weather. The winner was Mike Smith, flying his extensively modified Beech Bonanza and beating two VariEzes, Cessnas and Pipers.

Encouragement from the National Aeronautic Association led to many attempts in 1982 on FAI speed records by racing aeroplanes. In May Dan Mortensen set a Class C.1.b speed record over a 3km straight course, achieving 377.62km/hr (234.64mph) in his Amsoil-Rutan Racer biplane. Following the Lowers-Baker-Falck 500, two of the competitors went for records on the L-B-F course: Chuck Andrews, flying the VW-powered Monex, set two records in the new Class C.1.a/o, with 297.7km/hr (184.99mph) for 100km and 293.05km/hr (182.09mph) for 500km. A few days later A. J. Smith flew his AJ-2 over 500km at a speed of 407.5km/hr (253.23mph) to set a record in Class C.1.b. In October Mortensen took the Class C.1.b. 100km mark with 375.49km/hr (233.32mph), and then Paul Musso flew his Formula One racer *Real Sporty* at 377.33km/hr (234.46mph) over a 15km straight course for a Class C.1.a. record.

As a whole the 1982 American air racing season was highly competitive, completely safe and fun for the pilots, crews and fans. With more of the same expected in 1983, the sport appears to be in very good health.

The Skunk Works story

Jay Miller

The F-104 Starfighter was the Skunk Works' first major post-war creation. The ultimate F-104 design study resulted in the CL-1200 Lancer proposal. This design, shown in full-scale mock-up form, came within days of being approved for prototype construction. Hungry for a contract, Kelly Johnson even offered to sell the aircraft to the Air Force as a testbed under the X-27 designation. *(Lockheed)*

The birth of Lockheed's famous yet enigmatic Skunk Works, otherwise known as the ADP (Advanced Development Projects) office, is directly attributable to the company's renowned aircraft designer, Clarence L. "Kelly" Johnson. It was named after the foul-smelling factory in Al Capp's "Li'l Abner" comic strip, which appeared regularly in newspapers around the world for almost a half century. (Al Capp used the spelling "Skonk Works"; Lockheed has since trademarked "Skunk Works" to avoid possible copyright problems.) But whatever you call it, the fact remains that the

Skunk Works has grown in forty years from a small advanced design bureau with a local reputation into an organisation acclaimed the world over for its creativity and technological daring.

The words "Skunk Works" have become virtually synonymous with advanced development in general and covert activities in particular. Similar facilities at such companies as General Dynamics and Hayes International Corporation (working on low-visibility/high-technology aircraft modifications) have also become known as Skunk Works, and almost all the major US aerospace manufacturers lay claim to tightly knit talent pools run on the same lines. First and finest of them all, though, is Lockheed-California's Burbank division, which set the style of extraordinarily tight security and high productivity. Lockheed's unique facility, guarded in some areas by airlock doors and accessible only to select personnel with high security clearances, is one of the most security-conscious operations in the aerospace business. Information leaks are virtually unknown, and if one occurs its source is quickly discovered and plugged.

This level of security has two purposes. First and foremost, it is to protect developments that could prove to be of military benefit to the United States. Second, it guards those discoveries that Lockheed could turn to its own commercial advantage.

During the formative years of the Skunk Works Kelly Johnson wrote down the facility's 14 operating rules. These were: almost complete control by the project manager; a strong but small project office; an "almost vicious" restriction of the number of people connected with any given project; a simple, flexible drawing system; minimum paperwork; thorough and periodic cost review; authority to subcontract; tight inspection; flight testing; prior specifications; timely funding; mutual trust; tight security; and rewards based on performance.

The Skunk Works has no exact birthdate, since it came into being over a long period and also because it was not the result of any formal declaration. Rather its creation paralleled Kelly Johnson's ascent through the ranks of the company. A stickler for complete freedom and absolute secrecy during preliminary design and development and early flight test, Johnson evolved the Skunk Works philosophy for prototyping and pre-production over many years.

Johnson entered the aerospace business after graduating as an aeronautical engineer from the University of Michigan. In 1933, in a rare stroke of Depression-era luck, he was hired as an aerodynamicist by the fledgeling Lockheed Aircraft Company. His knack for producing convincing arguments in favour of his projects soon brought him to prominence, and it was not long before his words were being borne out by performance. Lockheed aircraft designs, many rising either directly or indirectly from the Johnson drawing board, invariably proved to be exceptional in performance, durability and value for money.

In the late 1930s Johnson started work on the P-38 Lightning or *Gabelschwanz Teufel* (Fork-Tailed Devil), as Luftwaffe pilots would eventually refer to it. The Lightning proved to be long-legged, rugged and respected by its pilots. Though not his first successful design, the P-38 was nonetheless a major stepping stone for Johnson and represented an important foot in the door for future dealings with the War Department.

In the spring of 1943 the adolescent Burbank advanced design facility, still working night and day on improved derivatives of the P-38 while exploring such exotic notions as supersonic flight and jet propulsion, was invited to submit proposals for a fighter designed around the British Halford H.1B turbojet engine. The request for a prototype was officially issued on May 17, 1943, and after a month of negotiations construction of the aircraft began.

Johnson, now leader of a design and construction team that eventually consisted of 23 engineers and 105 assembly personnel, had promised to have the prototype ready no more than 180 days after the signing of the contract. Determined to keep his word, Johnson removed his group from the main Lockheed design and assembly centre and installed them in a temporary building near the wind tunnel at Lockheed Plant B-1. Nearby was a plastics plant and its associated odour, and the name Skunk Works quickly caught on. Johnson was not particularly happy with it but there was little he could do: time and popularity eventually meant that the name stuck for good.

Johnson and his team beat their imposed 180-day deadline. Astonishingly, prototype XP-80 44-83020, nicknamed *Lulu Belle*, took to the air for the first time on January 8, 1944, just two days short of the 180 days. It was only by adopting a novel approach to the prototyping process that Johnson had been able to achieve an apparently impossible task. He won a free hand in his choice of personnel, materials and methods. What is more, his requests were given priority over virtually all others within the company and the War Department. In later years Johnson would condense his approach into one short sentence: "Be quiet, be quick, and be on time."

The eventual massive success of the quick and agile P-80 added to Johnson's growing reputation and brought with it more contracts for new design studies. His methods were also applied elsewhere and with equal success. Similar high-priority programmes were granted the same rights as XP-80, and without exception they came in on time and under budget.

Following successful development of the P-80 the Skunk Works moved on to a number of projects which expanded the team's experience without leading to major production contracts. One of the more noteworthy examples was the aesthetically pleasing but sadly deficient XF-90. Ill-conceived and burdened with unrealistic specifications, the XF-90 programme resulted in two prototype aircraft and a realisation that the day of the super-heavy escort fighter was fast drawing to a close.

With this in mind, in mid-1950 the Skunk Works started design development work on the first of many lightweight fighters optimised for clear-air interception. Later referred to as point-defence interceptors, these aircraft had relatively short range, high acceleration, good manoeuvrability and modest armament.

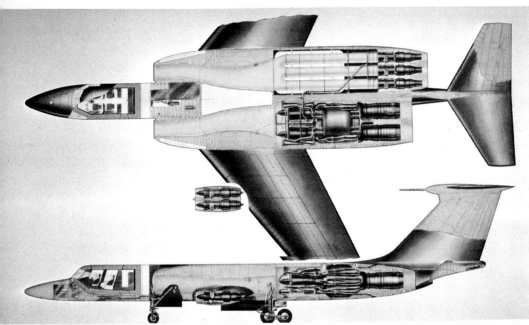

Above: **The second of the two prototype XF-104s. The preliminary Skunk Works designs proposed for what became the U-2 were based on the XF-104 fuselage with skid landing gear.** (*Lockheed*)

Left: **Like many major US aerospace manufacturers in the 1950s, Lockheed jumped on the nuclear-powered aircraft bandwagon. Shown here is one of many proposals produced by the Skunk Works over a period of nearly ten years.** (*Lockheed*)

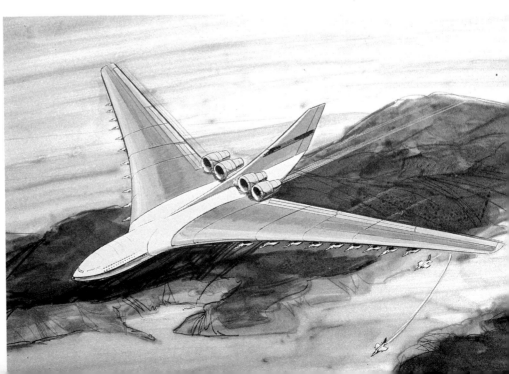

Above: **Among the more recently released design studies from the Skunk Works is this Mach 3+ interceptor, with low radar signature, blended-body aerodynamics, and two-dimensional exhaust nozzles.** (*Lockheed*)

Right: **For many years a colleague of the great Clarence L. "Kelly" Johnson, Ben Rich is now director of the Skunk Works.** (*Lockheed*)

Johnson's ultimate study in this series eventually resulted in one of the world's most unusual post-war fighters, the F-104 Starfighter. The world's first production aircraft capable of achieving speeds in excess of Mach 2 in level flight, the F-104 catapulted Johnson and his bureau back into the limelight. It also did wonders for Lockheed's performance on the stock market.

As with the P-80, the basic F-104 design permitted the exploration of a variety of configurations. These investigations resulted in relatively minor changes permitting increased fuel and weapons loads, and, in a few instances, looked at some truly radical ideas. Among the latter were a Vtol-capable F-104, a series of drone F-104s, and a variant capable of super-high-altitude cruising flight.

The U-2, as the high-altitude variant of the F-104 eventually came to be known, put the Skunk Works on the map. But it was almost by chance that the U-2 came into existence at all, as the original high-altitude reconnaissance aircraft project had been steered away from the largest US aerospace companies and entrusted instead to some of the lesser concerns. Bell had in fact won the original non-competition for development of an ultra-high-altitude reconnaissance aircraft to be used in clandestine overflights of unfriendly territory. The Bell design, known in-house as the Model 67 and designated X-16 by the Central Intelligence Agency and the Air Force, was well down the road towards first flight when it was cancelled.

Lockheed set out to corner this valuable contract when the existence of a high-altitude recce aircraft programme was leaked to Kelly Johnson. Thus armed, Johnson met well placed friends in the Department of Defence and convinced them that they should consider this hurriedly created submission. At first this was rejected by the Wright Air Development Centre, which had nurtured the Bell programme from birth and felt that the Johnson proposal, powered by the unknown General Electric J73, offered less capability and greater risk. However, the Johnson aircraft, known to Lockheed as the CL-282 and based on the still-immature F-104, was given a second chance when the extremely high-powered Killian intelligence committee took a shine to it.

Following presentations of the virtues of the Lockheed and Bell designs (and those of the interim RB-57D), it was the Lockheed proposal that went into the briefcases of representatives sent to explain the new recce programme to President Eisenhower. Some $35 million was then released from a classified Presidential fund and 20 U-2s were ordered.

When Johnson heard that the project was to go ahead he requested and received the same *carte blanche* given to several other Skunk Works projects. Such was the programme's exceptional political sensitivity, companies supplying parts were given the minimum of information. More preferable still, components were manufactured behind closed doors at Burbank. Final assembly of the prototype U-2, following delivery of major sub-assemblies by C-124 transport, took place at a new, classified and extraordinarily remote flight test facility called Watertown Strip and located next to Groom Dry Lake in north-eastern Nevada. Later nick-named "The Ranch," this facility was to become the flight-test extension of the Skunk Works.

In a typical example of the Skunk Works philosophy in action, the prototype U-2, with well-known Lockheed test pilot Tony Levier at the controls, took to the air for the first time on August 1, 1955, just eight months after project go-ahead. Production of the remaining aircraft followed, and after completion and initial flight tests at The Ranch they were turned over to the CIA for operational flight trials and evaluation. The first of some 30 clandestine missions over the Soviet Union began shortly thereafter.

While production of the U-2 continued at Burbank and several other Lockheed-controlled facilities, Johnson and the Skunk Works team began to explore more advanced configurations designed to penetrate unfriendly airspace. At the same time, British engineer Randolph Samuel Rae, employed by the Summers Gyroscope Company in Santa Monica, California, submitted to the USAF's Air Research and Development Command (ARDC) a proposal for a three-stage propeller-turbine-powered aircraft fuelled by liquid hydrogen and liquid oxygen. Rae's proposal was reviewed by the ARDC and in October 1955, following the acquisition of rights to Rae's propulsion ideas, the Garrett Corporation was contracted to explore its possibilities.

Funding for an aircraft design study based on propulsion by liquid hydrogen powerplants led to a two-month study subcontract for the Skunk Works, which was to be responsible for the airframe. The resulting preliminary design, known as the CL-325-1, had a thin, straight wing and a very slender fuselage. Propulsion was to be provided by two liquid hydrogen powerplants generating 20kN (4,500lb st) each. The aircraft was expected to cruise at Mach 2.25 at an altitude of 30,480m (100,000ft) over a range of 5,630km (3,500 miles). Further studies eventually led to the CL-325-2 but by mid-1957, interest in the programme had waned as it dawned on the Air Force that the development of the powerplant would be more difficult than expected.

In the meantime, the Skunk Works, under the direction of Johnson and fellow Lockheed engineer Ben Rich, forged ahead with still more advanced hydrogen-fuelled designs of their own, including the extraordinary CL-400. This aircraft, with a wing span of 25.53m (83ft 9in), a length of 50.24m (164ft 10in) and a gross take-off weight of 31,730kg (69,955lb), was a reconnaissance platform offering a cruising speed of Mach 2.5 over a range of approximately 4,023km (2,500 miles). Lockheed, with Johnson spearheading the effort, managed in April 1956 to secure an Air Force contract (under the ultra-secret Suntan liquid hydrogen-fuelled aircraft programme) calling for the development and construction of two prototype CL-400s.

Eighteen months was allowed for the completion of these aircraft (to be followed by six production examples), and work soon reached fever pitch at Burbank. But less than a year after work started Johnson began to develop serious doubts about the project, and particularly about the practicality of liquid hydrogen as an aircraft fuel. Finally, in October 1957, he recommended to the Air Force that the programme be cancelled and replaced by one with a more conventional basis.

The result was a new CIA-sponsored programme intended to produce a more secure platform for newly developed optical and non-optical sensors. Several remarkable designs were eventually proposed, including General Dynamics' Mach 6-cruise Fish and Kingfish ramjet-powered deltas and a US Navy inflatable rubber machine, also powered by ramjets. But Lockheed's slightly more conservative all-titanium double delta, code-named Oxcart, eventually proved the winner.

The Lockheed aircraft, known in-house as the A-12 and soon to become the world's first aircraft capable of Mach 3+ cruise, was rolled out in March 1962, some 27 months after go-ahead. Lou Schalk was at the controls when it flew for the first time, on April 26, 1962, from Groom Lake. A-12 flight testing proved a long and painful business that resulted in the loss of a large part of the A-12 fleet, though fortunately no pilot died. The Skunk Works remained deeply involved during this period, with Johnson interesting himself particularly in the highly classified operational facets of the programme.

Many variations to the basic A-12 theme were pre-

Below: **The only in-flight photograph of the single-seat Lockheed A-12 to be released to date shows 60-6932, the ninth aircraft in the series, during a Lockheed test flight.** (Lockheed)

Bottom: **A single A-12 was modified to two-seat trainer configuration by the Skunk Works. This aircraft is shown in storage at Palmdale, California.** (John Andrews)

Left: **A total of three YF-12A interceptor testbeds were manufactured by the Skunk Works.** (*Lockheed*)

Below: **SR-71A 64-17976 shoots a touch-and-go at Randolph AFB.** (*Jay Miller/Aerofax*)

sented to the DoD and other US Government agencies, of which only two are known to have reached fruition: the YF-12A interceptor testbed and the SR-71 reconnaissance aircraft. The former, a heavily modified derivative of the A-12, incorporated a Hughes AN/ASG-18 tracking radar in the nose and had provision for the advanced Hughes GAR-9 (AIM-47A) air-to-air missile. Three YF-12As were built, of which two were eventually destroyed during flight tests. The sole survivor is now on display at the USAF Museum in Dayton, Ohio.

The SR-71 represents the ultimate operational aircraft to roll out of the Skunk Works shop. Though not as fast in cruise as its A-12 predecessor (which had a maximum speed of Mach 3.6 at 28,950m; 95,000ft), the SR-71 is a significantly more refined aircraft and has accommodation for two crew members instead of the A-12's one. It can carry some 46,182lit (12,200 US gal) of JP-7 fuel internally, giving a Mach 3+ cruising range of 5,230km (3,250 miles).

The astonishing range of the Skunk Works' abilities

was demonstrated anew in 1979, when the first information about the enigmatic D-21 hypersonic cruise drone was leaked by the DoD. Long out of operational service by then, the D-21 was conceived late in the A-12 programme as a means of extending that aircraft's reconnaissance capabilities. The objective was to penetrate unfriendly airspace in search of intelligence without exposing a pilot to the dangers of such a mission — or the US Government to the potential embarrassment of his being captured. The drone was designed to be actively controlled only during certain parts of its flight and, following completion of the mission, would eject its sensor payload for mid-air retrieval. The drone itself would then be destroyed.

The Marquardt ramjet-powered D-21 was intended originally to be transported by and launched from A-12 carrier aircraft. Two A-12s were modified for this mission, with the drone mounted on a pylon between the A-12's vertical fins. But the programme got off to a bad start when a mid-1966 accident caused the death of an A-12 observer and led to the loss of the A-12/D-21

Top: **There is very little to mar the outstanding aerodynamic cleanliness of the awesome SR-71A. The blended body aerodynamics are plainly visible in this head-on view.** (*Jay Miller/Aerofax*)

Above: **Perhaps the least known of the Skunk Works' acknowledged products is the D-21 drone. Capable of achieving speeds in excess of Mach 5, the D-21 was powered by a Marquardt ramjet engine and normally launched from a Boeing B-52H.** (*Ben Knowles/Jay Miller/Aerofax*)

combination. Later developments led to the use of Boeing B-52Hs as carrier aircraft.

With the exception of renewed U-2 production in 1967 and 1982 (the U-2R and TR-1 respectively), and development of the QT-2/Q-Star, the Skunk Works has deliberately left centre stage in an effort to divert attention from its current, highly secret activities. Foremost among these is the design and development of aircraft with low radar signatures and embodying advanced composites in their structures. It is now rumoured that one aspect of this "Stealth" programme is an active rather than passive electronic countermeasures capability. At least three testbed aircraft, said to be single-seaters each powered by two J85s mounted on the upper surfaces of small ogival wings, have been flight-tested at Groom Lake and one other classified centre in Nevada. Though all three are said to have been destroyed in accidents, additional testbeds are either under construction or currently in flight test.

Kelly Johnson officially retired from Lockheed and the inimitable Skunk Works in 1975, promising to

remain active as a consultant. The reins to the world's foremost advanced aircraft design bureau were then turned over to the brilliant Ben Rich, Johnson's relatively unacknowledged colleague on virtually every Skunk Works project of significance since the early 1950s. Rich, who still directs the Skunk Works, has stayed unfailingly true to the Johnson motto of "Be quiet, be quick, and be on time".

(The author would like to acknowledge the valuable assistance of associates Bob Ferguson of the Lockheed-California Company, John Andrews of the Testor Corporation and René Francillon PhD. A special thanks also to Ben Rich, director of Lockheed's deservedly famous Advanced Development Projects office.)

Top left: **Two QT-2s were first flown in August 1967 as quiet observation aircraft. One prototype is seen here during the early days of the flight test programme, when the aircraft was still painted white. Repainting and use of a new designation (QT-2PC) took place before the aircraft was shipped to Vietnam. It remains probably the quietest powered aircraft ever to fly.** (Lockheed)

Above: **Both QT-2s survived their two tours of duty in Vietnam and were returned to the US for continuing military service. Becoming redundant to Army requirements, they were transferred to the Navy, which used them (under the X-26B designation) as roll-coupling trainers. One aircraft was eventually cannibalised to support the other and the survivor eventually went to the Army Aviation Museum.** (Dave Menard)

Left: **Continuing development by the Skunk Works of its QT series led to the Q-Star. Incorporating significantly more Lockheed-manufactured parts than its predecessors, it offered superior performance and better ground handling. But production contracts failed to materialise and the programme was terminated.** (Lockheed)

Right: **The only member of the QT/Q-Star family to enter production was the YO-3. Developed by the Skunk Works as a sensor-system transport with extraordinarily quiet in-flight performance, the YO-3A served well in Vietnam and remains in service with a number of non-military US government agencies.** (*Lockheed*)

Below: **Lockheed TR-1 seen during the roll-out ceremony in 1981.** (*US Air Force/Department of Defence*)

Space goes commercial

Reginald Turnill

With the successful completion of America's seventh Shuttle flight (STS-7) in June 1983, six satellites had been deployed from its capacious cargo bay with such accuracy that at least two of them could expect an extra two years of operational life — a bonus worth many millions to their operators. Canada and Indonesia paid Nasa $11 million each for the launch of their satellites on STS-7. This is only a small proportion of the total launch costs, but it's a start. Launch costs are difficult to estimate: around $250 million if you include research and development, perhaps $70 million in current dollars if you write them off.

During the first seven mission, 19 astronauts — one of whom, the irrepressibly cheerful Bob Crippen, had flown twice — had demonstrated that the Shuttle could be used as a base for spacewalking and station-building. Dr Sally Ride, at 32 the youngest-ever US astronaut as well as the first US spacewoman, had proved that satellites could be retrieved and repaired in orbit.

Commercial operations actually began in April 1983 with STS-5, on which the crew despatched two communications satellites for domestic use in Canada and America to their geostationary orbits, and sent back the message: "We deliver". Having completed a similar performance, the seventh crew then deployed Germany's Spas-01 satellite, performed a five-hour space ballet with it before retrieving it with Canada's versatile robot arm, and sent back another message: "We collect and deliver". Nasa's Shuttle manager, General "Abe" Abrahamson, could fairly claim that America's planned revolution in space had been achieved.

But the USA is far from being alone in the commercial launcher business. Two days before the STS-7 launch, Europe's Ariane recovered from its 1982 setback with a perfect launch from Kourou, successfully deploying ECS-1, Europe's first communications satellite. With it went Oscar-10, an amateur radio satellite, demonstrating Ariane's ability to carry out dual launches and thus halve the customer's costs. Anticipating this success, and the stiff competition Ariane would represent in the fight for commercial payloads, Nasa had a few days beforehand sent Orbiter

108

Left: *Challenger* **photographed from the Spas-01 free-flying satellite during STS-7.** (*Nasa*)

Right: **Spas-01 securely grappled by the Remote Manipulator System (RMS) arm in the course of the STS-7 demonstration of the Shuttle's ability to recover satellites for maintenance and repair.** (*Nasa*)

Below: **Precision launch of Indonesia's Palapa-B communications satellite, seen passing straight up in front of the tile-clad leading edge of** *Challenger*'s **fin. Visible in the foreground are several "Getaway Special" experiment canisters and the stowed RMS arm.** (*Nasa*)

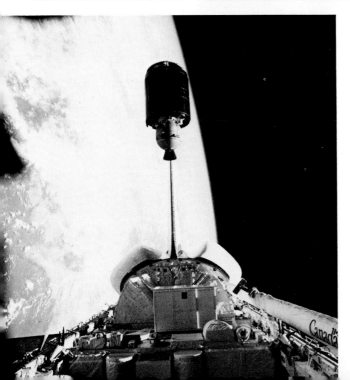

prototype *Enterprise*, mounted on top of its Boeing 747 carrier, around Europe on a Show-the-Shuttle tour. It duly stole the Paris Show, and rather unexpectedly led to the Russians cancelling their own participation there, since they apparently did not wish to display their now familiar aircraft beneath *Enterprise*'s truly enormous shadow.

Backstage promises by Nasa that if Shuttle is chosen for important launches it will carry foreign astronauts as accompanying payload specialists had their effect: Britain, hesitating over the rival commercial and political merits of using Shuttle or Ariane to launch the Skynet-4 military satellite in 1985, seems to have been persuaded by the offer.

At the same time, the Soviet Union entered the race to commercialise space by announcing that Protons were available at $24 million each to compete with Shuttle and Ariane for Inmarsat launches. As all these launchers are at present subsidised, it is impossible to find out just what a commercial launch is likely to cost the user when things settle down; but the current Soviet figure is probably a reasonable guide. Plans by US private-enterprise groups to offer commercial versions of Atlas-Centaur, Delta, Titan and even the Minuteman ICBM were probably based on expectations that Ariane would fail, and the companies would appear to have little hope of competing either commercially or politically against European and Soviet opposition.

The current year saw Nasa's traditional policy of conducting space exploration "for all mankind," with full details of mission objectives and their results available to all, coming under increasing pressure. Short of money, Nasa has already allowed the US Air Force to

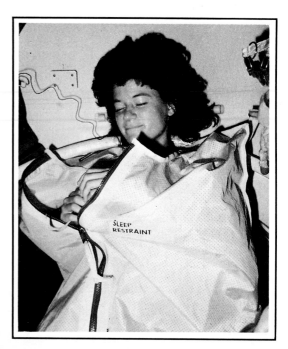

Left: **America's first woman astronaut, Dr Sally Ride, sleeps in the secure grasp of the Orbiter's sleep restraint system. Other Shuttle astronauts prefer to be anchored only by the upper body or feet when they sleep.** (*Nasa*)

Below left: **STS-6 mission specialist Story Musgrave at work in *Challenger*'s barn-sized payload bay. Musgrave and Donald Peterson carried out the Shuttle programme's first EVA, demonstrating that astronauts can perform complex tasks while outside the Orbiter's habitable areas.** (*Nasa*)

Below: **Orbiter prototype *Enterprise* was present at the Paris Salon as a reminder that Europe's Ariane faces stiff competition in the fight for satellite-launching business.**

establish classified areas and control rooms at the Kennedy and Johnson space centres in return for the financial benefits of such collaboration. Now the big US contractors are increasingly pointing out that, since America has invested over $150 billion in 25 years in pioneering space techniques, the commercial benefits should not be given away free to foreign competitors. Some of the most spectacular of those benefits may be with us soon: space platforms capable of producing materials and medicines far superior to those obtainable in normal gravity on earth could be no more than four years away.

The most striking example of what is possible in this direction is provided by the results of the Elec-

trophoresis Operations in Space (EOS) experiments carried out on STS-4, 6 and 7 as part of a Nasa/McDonnell Douglas effort to provide an opportunity for private enterprise to develop commercial applications. Johnson & Johnson, the pharmaceutical group, have had a secret agreement with McDonnell Douglas for some years past because the improved separation techniques available in zero-g for producing much purer vaccines offer real hopes for a breakthrough in the treatment of diseases like leukaemia and diabetes. By STS-6 not only had purification of biological materials

Left: **Mission patch for STS-9/Spacelab 1. This mission is notable in a number of respects: first flight of Europe's Spacelab; first flight by a European in a Western spacecraft; first launch of six people together in one craft; and a record sixth flight by mission commander John Young.** (*Nasa*)

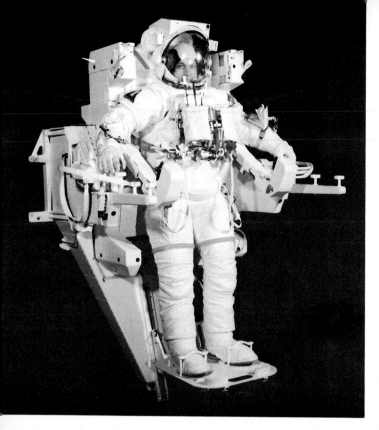

Bruce McCandless will demonstrate the Manned Manoeuvring Unit (MMU) during STS-11. Success in these trials is crucial to the planned repair of the Solar Maximum Mission (SMM) satellite, to be carried out by George Nelson or Terry Hart on STS-13. *(Nasa)*

years of flying their scientific experiments on Soviet spacecraft, French scientists probably have more all-round knowledge than the US of micro-gravity processing. There is also much American concern at France's detailed proposals to market throughout Europe and Africa images from Spot, her advanced earth-resources satellite due for Ariane launch next year. America's pioneering Landsat programme is suffering increasingly from a combination of technical problems and US Government dithering about commercialising the service. While the latest US reports say that the commercial demand for such services has been overestimated, France has confidently identified 60 potential user countries needing a total 100,000 images a year at $500-1,000 per scene.

France's Echograph machine, developed at a cost of Fr100 million and operated by "spationaute" Jean-Loup Chrétien aboard Salyut 7 in 1982, may even have put France ahead in studies of the baffling phenomenon of spacesickness, and Nasa is negotiating to fly it aboard the Shuttle in the near future.

The success of Germany's cheap but efficient Shuttle Pallet Satellite (Spas-01), designed by only 15 MBB scientists for a mere $13 million to demonstrate how private enterprise can make use of space, has only added to US alarm. It was Sally Ride's dexterity with the Canadian robot arm which enabled Spas to be deployed and retrieved, but the fact is that five years ago Germany identified the opportunity to develop this new kind of satellite and persuaded Nasa to fly it for nothing.

With hindsight, Germany was equally perceptive 10

Dr Judy Resnik, America's second woman astronaut and mission specialist on STS-12. The crew for this flight, the first by Orbiter *Discovery* (OV-103), will include McDonnell Douglas electrophoresis project engineer Charles Walker, the first payload specialist to come from private industry. *(Nasa)*

in a mid-deck facility operated by the astronauts been increased four times, but 700 times as much material was being separated than would be possible in similar ground-based units. Three more mid-deck tests will include the sending of 35-year-old Charles Walker, McDonnell Douglas's chief EOS test engineer, on STS-12 as the first commercial payload specialist. His job will be to run EOS as a prototype production unit continuously throughout the five-day mission. He is expected to bring back enough vaccine to start clinical tests on human subjects. A free-flying commercial production unit, mounted on a Spas-type satellite and visited every six months by Shuttle crews to deliver raw materials and collect separated products, is likely to appear well before the target date of 1987.

The unexpected decision to send Walker on a Shuttle mission was inspired not only by the success of the tests so far, but because of alarm among some American companies at the speed and efficiency with which some foreign countries — notably Germany, France and Japan — are moving into space commercialisation.

France, in addition to providing the finance and incentive to produce Ariane as an independent launcher, has for many years been the only other country apart from the US and Soviet Union to have an effective, well funded national space agency. After 15

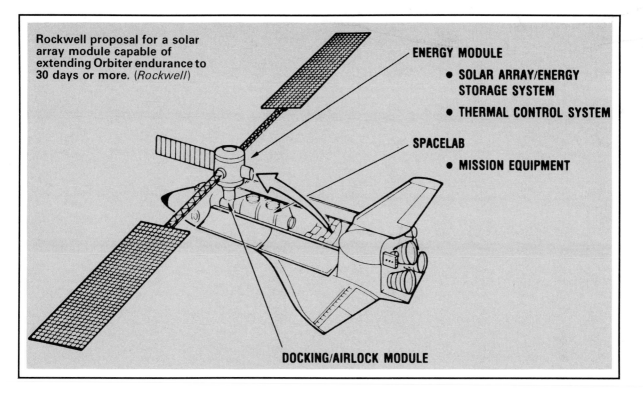

Rockwell proposal for a solar array module capable of extending Orbiter endurance to 30 days or more. (*Rockwell*)

ENERGY MODULE
- **SOLAR ARRAY/ENERGY STORAGE SYSTEM**
- **THERMAL CONTROL SYSTEM**

SPACELAB
- **MISSION EQUIPMENT**

DOCKING/AIRLOCK MODULE

years ago in choosing to become the main supporter of Spacelab, developed by ESA as its contribution to America's Shuttle programme. Not only has Germany been taking advantage of Nasa's "Getaway Special" opportunities to carry out a whole series of crystal-growing and materials-processing experiments on successive Shuttle flights, but she is paying for two national Spacelab missions in 1985-86 which seem likely to bring all this research to the productive stage.

Amid these warnings that they should not give too much away to the competition, it is not surprising that Nasa's managers nowadays seem somewhat confused. If they are to get Presidential go-ahead by the end of this year for development of a space station to be operational in 1990-91, as they expect, they must produce evidence that there will be international help with the funding. Britain, apparently content with its limited success in producing and marketing individual satellites and their equipment, appears little interested, and if there is insufficient support for collaboration among the 11 European Space Agency nations, the indications are that Germany and France may well participate nationally instead of through ESA. That way they would not have to share the benefits of their space station contributions.

All these developments have led to a new urgency to extend the Shuttle's mission time. Nasa's aim has always been to use space stations, not the Shuttle, to match the Soviets' ability to run long-duration missions like the record 211-day effort in Salyut 7. But with a US space station up to 10 years away, the nine-day Spacelab flight this autumn looks insignificant indeed

when compared with the Soviet capability. Rockwell has therefore come up with a scheme to extend Shuttle stay time to 15-18 days within two years at a cost of only $60 million, developing what it calls a cryo-wafer kit (cryogenic fuel cells) capable of providing enough extra power for 6.67 days. Stays of up to 45 days could be achieved by 1988 at a cost of $200-$250 million by means of a solar array which could be parked in orbit. Fitted with a modified airlock and mid-deck, Shuttle would dock with the array, presumably after deploying any satellites carried.

Whether or not these proposals are adopted, the coming year should see America's space activities looking much more competitive when compared with those of the Soviets. Astronaut Bruce McCandless will leap to fame on STS-11, belying his grey hair by becoming the first man to try out the Manned Manoeuvring Unit, though he will probably still be tethered to the Shuttle cargo bay. Bob Crippen, making his third flight, will command STS-13 in June 1984, when at long last an attempt will be made to reach and repair the Solar Maximum Mission satellite. Either George Nelson or Terry Hart will make the first untethered MMU flight to capture the tumbling SMM.

By then all of NASA's 78 astronauts should have been assigned to specific missions, with another dozen selected to follow them up. Most of them expect to average two flights a year. With eight women among them, General Abrahamson's second milestone for women astronauts will be achieved within two years: no one will notice when women fly, because they will be doing the same professional job as men.

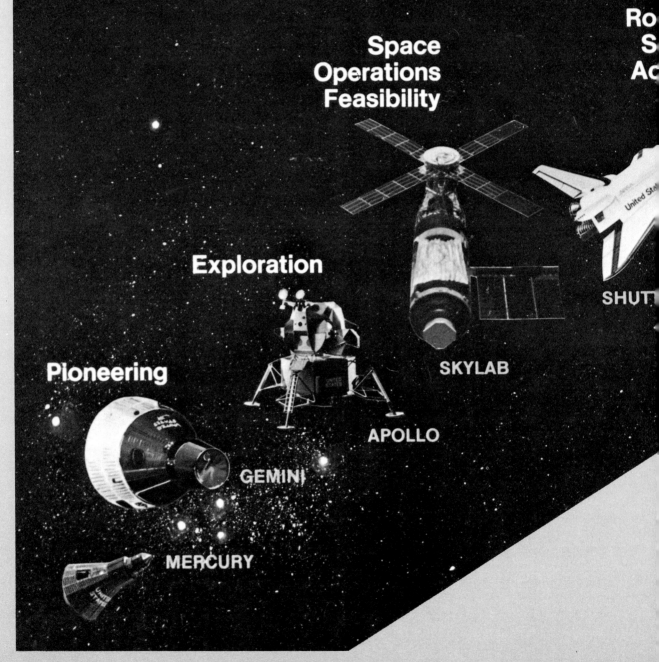

Strategy for Space

Space
Operations
Feasibility

Ro
S
Ac

Exploration

Pioneering

SKYLAB

SHUT

APOLLO

GEMINI

MERCURY

114

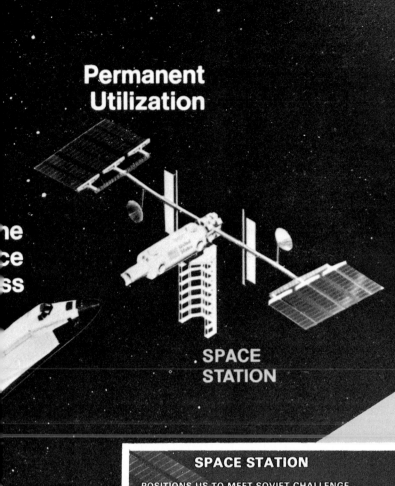

Permanent Utilization

SPACE STATION

Left: **Nasa view of the evolution of the American manned spaceflight programme, from Mercury to the eagerly awaited permanent space station.** (*Nasa*)

Below: **Proposed configuration for a first-generation US permanent space station. The list of capabilities includes missions that on present indications are unlikely to be tackled until the 21st century.** (*Nasa*)

SPACE STATION

POSITIONS US TO MEET SOVIET CHALLENGE

SETS NEW LEVEL OF CAPABILITY WITH OPTIONS TO GROW

PROVIDES FOUNDATION FOR STRATEGIC ALTERNATIVES

DEMONSTRATES LEADERSHIP TO THE FREE WORLD

STIMULATES ADVANCED TECHNOLOGY

DRAMATICALLY EXPANDS COMMERCIAL OPPORTUNITIES IN SPACE

PROVIDES BROAD OPPORTUNITY FOR INTERNATIONAL COOPERATION

CAPABILITIES

NATIONAL LABORATORY ON-ORBIT OPERATIONS

RETURN TO THE MOON
MARS SAMPLE RETURN MISSION

LARGE FACILITIES AT GEOSYNCHRONOUS ORBIT

Shuttle flight log (as at July 1, 1983)

Mission/OV*	Launch date	Crew	Duration (days, hours, min)	Details
STS-1 102	12.04.81	Young, Crippen	02.06.21	Near-perfect 1st flight
STS-2 102	12.11.81	Engle, Truly	02.06.13	5-day mission halved by fuel-cell fault
STS-3 102	22.03.82	Lousma, Fullerton	08.00.05	Extra day because of storm at Northrop landing ground
STS-4 102	27.07.82	Mattingly, Hartsfield	07.01.10	1st concrete landing. SRBs lost. DoD package failed
STS-5 102	11.11.82	Brand, Overmyer, Allen, Lenoir	05.02.14	1st operational flight. SBS-3, Anik-C3 deployed. EVA failed
STS-6 099	05.04.83	Weitz, Bobko, Peterson, Musgrave	05.00.23	Delayed 3 months by engine leaks, etc. TDRS-1. 1st EVA
STS-7 099	18.06.83	Crippen, Hauck, Ride, Fabian, Thagard	06.02.24	1st US woman, 1st satellite retrieval. Anik-C2, Palapa-B1 deployed
STS-8 099	30.08.83	Truly, Brandenstein, Bluford, Gardner, Thornton	06.01.25	Insat-1B
STS-9 102	30.10.83	Young, Shaw, Garriott, Parker, Lichtenberg, Merbold	09	Spacelab 1
STS-10 099		Mattingly, Shriver, Onizuka, Buchli, USAF PS		DoD, postponed due to IUS failure on STS-6
STS-11 099	31.01.84	Brand, Gibson, McCandless, Stewart, McNair	07	1st MMU with RMS by McCandless. LFC-1, Palapa-B2
STS-12 103	21.03.84	Hartsfield, Coats, Resnik, Hawley, Mullane, Walker (PS)	05	*Discovery*'s 1st flight. Resnik 2nd woman. MSL-1. 1st commercial PS
STS-13 099	18.04.84	Crippen, Scobee, Nelson, Hart, van Hoften	05	LDEF-1. SMM repair
STS-14 103	06.06.84	Bobko, Williams, Seddon, Hoffman, Griggs	07	Oast-1, Telesat-1, Syncom-4/1, payload opportunity
STS-15 102	03.07.84			Reflight opportunity
STS-16 099	01.08.84	Hauck, Walker, Allen, Gardner, Fisher	07	Spartan-1, Telstar-3C, SBS-4, Syncom-4/2
STS-17 103	29.08.84	4	07	Osta-3, ERBS, payload opportunity
STS-18 102	26.09.84	Overmyer, Gregory, Lind, Thagard, Thornton, 2 PS	06	Spacelab 3
STS-19 099	23.10.84	4	07	MSL-2, Telesat-8, Arabsat-1, payload opportunity
STS-20 103				Reflight opportunity
STS-21 099	19.12.84			DoD 85-1
STS-22 103	23.01.85			DoD 85-2

*OV = Orbiter Vehicle: 099 *Challenger*, 102 *Columbia*, 103 *Discovery*, 104 *Atlantis*.

RAF heavyweight contenders

Bill Gunston

There was a time when the RAF wrote Operational Requirements (ORs) and the British industry, consisting of numerous powerful companies, fought to produce the aircraft needed. Today all that has changed. ORs are still written but usually without the slightest chance of an aircraft being designed around any of them. The most that can be hoped for is that money can be found either to modify an existing RAF aircraft or to buy off the shelf from civil operators who are prepared to let the equipment go at the knock-down price the British Treasury is prepared to afford.

This procedure has already done much to improve the RAF's global airlift capability, which will soon include VC10s, TriStars and stretched Hercules, all capable of acting as tankers. Flight refuelling was cru-

cial to the Falklands operation, and intensive flying ate severely into the limited remaining structural life of the Victor tankers (which have no capability as transports). With memories of that brilliantly fought but unwanted war fresh in the mind, the problem remains that the Falklands are still well over 13,100km (8,000 miles) from Britain, about as far as New York to New Zealand, and with only the single undulating runway of Wideawake Airfield on Ascension Island in between. Britain looks committed for the foreseeable future to maintaining a major air transport operation between the UK and the Falklands. Even though arriving air-

RAF Hercules C1 (background) alongside a stretched C3.

craft can now land on the improved Port Stanley runway, the mission is still a daunting one. It is totally uneconomic to use such equipment as the willing C-130 Hercules, no matter how it may be stretched or air-refuelled. After all, the "Herky Bird" was designed as a *tactical* airlifter.

What are the really long-range transports now flying? The Lockheed C-5A Galaxy could just about carry its maximum payload on the longer sector of 6,850km (4,260 miles) between Britain and Wide-awake. It is ideal from such viewpoints as volumetric capacity, navigational aids and ability to use softer surfaces, but does not happen to be available. There is no chance of buying new C-5B (C-5N) aircraft when these appear from 1984, because inflation has pushed their price to several times the figure for the C-5A. The fleet of the latter (71 of the 81 built) are being rewinged, but the USAF has none to spare. As a pipe-dream, the ideal would be a second-hand C-5A bought without

engines and fitted with new Rolls-Royce RB.211-535E4s or H4s, equal in power to the TF39s at present fitted but saving several tons in installed weight, approximately 40 per cent in pod drag and at least 33 per cent in fuel burn. How about building ten or a dozen 535-engined Galaxies under licence? Regrettably, the cost would surely be prohibitive.

Another good aircraft would be the C-141 StarLifter, or better still a C-141 re-engined with two 535H4s. This type has a rather cramped body cross-section, the same as a C-130, but could carry a heavier load much faster with no difficulty on the longer sector. Again, the problem is the fact that there are no C-141s available.

Perhaps the best of all the off-the-shelf aircraft would be the Soviet Antonov An-22 Antei, which could carry its maximum payload of 80 tonnes (175,000lb) on the longer sector without difficulty, and again has excellent navigation and soft-field capability. Unfortunately it could hardly be more foreign, and the giant turboprops and their propellers are getting on and would give rise to problems. An An-22 with four Rolls-Royce 535H4s would be quite something, but hardly likely. Not many An-22s were built, and the tooling has probably been scrapped. Nor is there much chance of getting hold of the Il-76, though at least this fine aircraft is still in production. Very like the C-141, the Il-76 is very much more powerful and has much better acceleration and braking power, as well as a landing gear specially designed for off-airfield operation. It could handle the UK-Ascension sector with a 40-tonne load, and do considerably better with four RB.211-535Cs, as now

used on the Boeing 757. As with the C-141, a twin-RB.211 version (524D4s rated at 235.75kN; 53,000lb st each) would show a great range improvement, though perhaps for such missions two engines, even of a supremely reliable type, would be inadequate.

There are plenty of commercial aircraft with enough payload and range, including the 747 and 747SP, the DC-10-30CF, later TriStar 500s and perhaps the DC-8-72 or 73CF. All are less than ideal in having a main floor high off the ground and reached through a side door (except for the cargo 747, which has a swing-up nose). The big advantage of these aircraft is that all are available, most of them second-hand, and would pose no particular problems in being fitted into RAF service.

Soviet An-22s on exercise. (*Tass*)

119

Boeing 747-200F freighter in commercial use. The 747 could readily be fitted into RAF service.

As a last possibility, consideration could be given to a stretched C-130 with beefed-up or additional landing gear and fitted with a new centre section increasing the span to 47.85m (157ft) and fuel capacity to 41,000lit (9,000 Imp gal). At a take-off weight of about 95 tonnes (209,000lb) this would not have any severe field-length problems and could stick with the existing RAF engines and systems, the only new components being the centre section, larger fin and landing gear. However, the snag is that in trying to produce a big very-long-range airlifter it is silly to start with a small tactical one, no matter how good it may be.

One is reminded of the various proposals of 25 to 30 years ago for transports with laminar-flow wings giving such an improvement in drag that they could fly non-stop from England to Australia, getting on for half as far again as the distance between England and the Falklands. Such aircraft have always been judged impractical, because specks of dirt could destroy their special low-drag properties. In any case, today we cannot afford to build a new long-range airlifter for what appears to be a very specialised RAF requirement not shared by other air forces. But surely anything must be preferable to an air bridge totally dependent on air refuelling?

This is your master's voice . . .

David Mondey

One of the most exciting aviation research projects under way in the United States at present is General Dynamics' AFTI/F-16 programme. This exploration of promising new fighter aircraft techniques under the Advanced Fighter Technology Integration (AFTI) programme is being directed by the US Air Force Systems Command's Flight Dynamics Laboratory (FDL) at Wright-Patterson AFB, Ohio, with a General Dynamics F-16 being used as a testbed. Early control-configured vehicle (CCV) programmes sought to develop an intentionally unstable high-performance aircraft that would be extremely manoeuvrable, and the AFTI/F-16 is the first operationally equipped fighter to demonstrate the flight techniques made possible by this new technology. It can, for example, track a crossing target by sliding sideways without banking, enabling its pilot to continue firing without having to disengage and circle for a new attack.

One aspect of AFTI is potentially of the highest importance. Known as voice interaction, this covers voice warnings and command and promises to make the pilot more effective in combat by reducing cockpit workload. By freeing his hands of many routine jobs and giving him aural warning of problems, voice interaction will permit him to concentrate on events outside the cockpit. Voice warning attracts the pilot's immediate attention in an emergency, whereas he might miss a yellow (caution) or red (warning) light while trying to keep his gaze on enemy activities. Much work has already been done on this aspect of voice interaction, and by the autumn of 1983 all new F-16s will have voice warning of 20 different emergencies. This includes stall warning, and an F-16 pilot will hear the words "caution, caution" if a yellow master caution light comes on, and "warning, warning, warning, warning" whenever a red warning light is on.

The emphasis now is on perfecting voice command, which would allow the pilot to operate manual switches without taking either hand from crucial flight controls. Each pilot in AFTI has a personalised cassette which records his pronunciation of the command words. The pilot loads this into a cockpit data-transfer module, which carries his voice patterns to the voice command computer. This then stores them as individual word templates in a voice-recognition system. Before executing a command, the computer matches the pilot's spoken word with the pre-recorded template.

General Dynamics AFTI/F-16 fighter technology testbed.

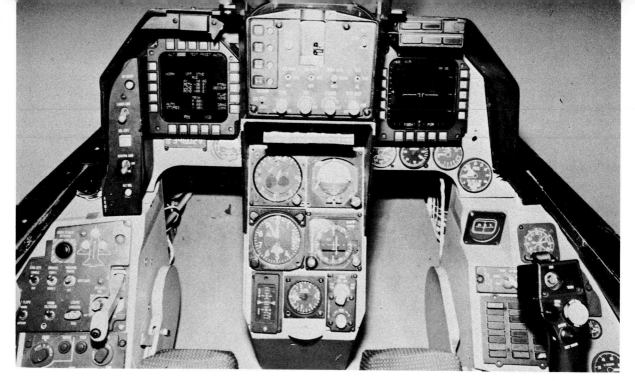

AFTI/F-16 cockpit simulator at the Fort Worth Division of General Dynamics. *(US Air Force)*

In the AFTI/F-16 the pilot activates the voice command system by means of a control button on the throttle. Speaking into his oxygen-mask microphone, he can use the voice command vocabulary to specify a variety of tasks. Since the voice command system is linked with the multiplexed multipurpose displays (MPD), any task operated by the pushbutton switches located around the MPDs can also be commanded in this way. An indication on the MPD confirms to the pilot that the task has been carried out.

Though development is going well, there are many problems to be solved before voice interaction becomes commonplace. Experimenters at the Air Force Aerospace Medical Research Laboratory (AFAMRL) are trying to determine whether cockpit environmental factors — direct and lateral g forces, vibration, and noise generated by airflow over the aircraft, cockpit systems and the pilot breathing into his oxygen mask — might affect the accuracy of a voice system. The studies are also intended to assess whether the stress of combat might so affect a pilot's speech that the system could not recognise it.

For this purpose AFAMRL scientists have recorded words spoken in the cockpit both in flight and during laboratory simulations of g forces, vibration and noise. The resulting tapes are being played into the voice command system in an effort to identify those factors which might reduce its reliability. If the present system does prove vulnerable it is hoped that it will be possible to solve the problem by altering the computer software to compensate for distortions in the received voice signal.

As well as supporting AFTI/F-16, the Flight Dynamics Laboratory's flight control division is also carrying out some fundamental voice command work of its own, addressing three questions. Can voice command work in any cockpit? What tasks are most appropriate for voice command? Is there any advantage in using voice command for certain tasks? Principal tool for this research is a laboratory model of the AFTI/F-16's voice hardware and audio tapes provided by AFAMRL. One experiment under way in early 1983 was seeking the best way of alerting a voice command system to begin accepting voice signals; alternatives being explored are variations of the throttle-mounted pushbutton and the use of code words.

Another important area of research centres on the voice recognition system. This must be fully fail-safe because of the similarities between words spoken casually in the cockpit and the control words in the system's vocabulary: "look out" and "lock out" for example. Choice of vocabulary is obviously of great importance, and is aimed as far as possible at the elimination of words, like "dive" and "five," which have similar sounds. The current experimental vocabulary comprises 36 words, ten of which were used for the first time on December 21, 1982, when USAF Lt-Col Harry Heimple was test-flying the AFTI/F-16. The expressions used in this initial check-out were "air-to-surface", "back", "five", "four", "inventory", "preset", "SMS", "six", "space", and "strafe." Plans called for the words to be spoken as pilot and cockpit were subjected to ever-increasing noise, vibration and g levels. It was intended that this initial phase would be followed in summer 1983 by demonstrations of the AFTI/F-16 pilots' ability to control switch selections, display formats and master modes with the full existing vocabulary of 36 words.

China: the dragon spreads its wings

Kenneth Munson

China, which gave the world the kite (in 1000 BC) and the rocket (1100 AD), is one of the world's oldest civilisations. Yet since man began to fly in the early years of this century her internal politics and lifestyle were such that no settled development of a national aircraft industry was possible until after the country came under Communist control in 1949. Aided then by the USSR, the Chinese began to establish a system of state aircraft and aero-engine factories. But their progress towards world status in the three decades which followed has been hampered by two traumatic events: the ideological split with the Soviet Union in 1960, which threw China back very much upon her own limited resources, and the pro-agriculture/anti-technology Cultural Revolution of 1966-69. In such a context, which has no parallel in the West, the Chinese aerospace industry has in a relatively short time accomplished much of which it can be proud.

Longest established of the Chinese aircraft factories are those at Shenyang and Harbin. The latter had its origins in the plant of the Manshu Aeroplane Manufacturing Company, one of several facilities established in Manchukuo (Manchuria) by the invading Japanese in 1938, which produced approximately 1,500 Ki-27 and Ki-84 fighters and about 700 Ki-79 trainers for the Japanese Army Air Force during 1941-45. A large flying training school was established by the Japanese at Shenyang (then known as Mukden) in 1940.

Shenyang

In the middle and late 1950s Shenyang produced under licence large numbers of several types of aircraft, the first of these being the Yak-18, for which an agreement was signed with the USSR in November 1952. In October 1954 this was followed by a licence for the Antonov An-2 general-purpose biplane, the Mil Mi-4 helicopter, and their ASh-62 and ASh-82 engines. A few Ilyushin Il-14 transports were also built, under the Chinese designation Yun-6.

The first jet aircraft built in China were the single-seat Mikoyan MiG-15bis and two-seat MiG-15UTI, neither with a Chinese designation. They were followed by the MiG-17F, known in China as the Jian-5 or J-5, and the MiG-17PF (Jian-5 Jia or J-5A). The MiG fighters and their Klimov VK-1 engines were produced at Shenyang, deliveries of both the MiG-15UTI and Jian-5 beginning in late 1956; by mid-1959 these were almost totally of Chinese manufacture. Several hundred MiG-15s (mostly UTIs) remain in service, and over 1,000 J-5/5As still equip 20 or more air regiments in the air-to-air and fighter-bomber roles. A small number of Jian-5s also continue in service with the Aviation of the People's Navy. Others, under the export designation F-5, were supplied to Albania (30), Kampuchea and North Vietnam.

The standard advanced trainer of the Chinese air forces, to which pupil pilots graduate after basic training on the Nanchang CJ-6, is a tandem two-seat version of the MiG-17. No such version was developed in the Soviet Union, and this aircraft, known as the Jianjiao-5 or JJ-5, is therefore unique to the Chinese industry. It combines the tandem cockpits and forward fuselage of the MiG-15UTI with the rest of the airframe of the MiG-17PF/J-5A, although it retains the latter's lipped intake, the small radome indicating provision for a radar-ranging gunsight in the front cockpit. An instructor's cockpit with dual controls and raised seat is installed to the rear of the standard pilot's cockpit. Other changes by comparison with the single-seat fighter include use of a non-afterburning Wopen-5 (Klimov VK-1A) turbojet rated at 26.48kN (5,952lb st); reduction of the armament to a single 23mm gun carried in a removable belly pack and with the barrel to the starboard side of the nosewheel doors; some modification of the fuel system; and the use of Chinese semi-automatic ejection seats. In addition to production for home use, China has exported the JJ-5, under the designations FT-5 and F-5T, to Bangladesh, Pakistan, the Sudan and Tanzania.

The present capability of China's aircraft industry was however first revealed openly by study of the Jian-6 single-seat fighters supplied to Pakistan in the latter 1960s, which were generally similar to the Soviet MiG-19SF. The Soviet MiG-19 prototype flew for the first time in mid-September 1953, and the initial production MiG-19 day fighter entered Soviet service in

In addition to over 40 Chinese air regiments, nine air defence and ground attack squadrons of the Pakistani Air Force are equipped with F-6 (Jian-6) fighters built at Shenyang and Tianjin. These late-production J-6Cs are identifiable by the bullet fairing under the rudder, housing a relocated brake parachute. *(John Fricker)*

early 1955. Though production in the USSR had been phased out by the end of the 1950s, a licence agreement for its manufacture in China had been signed in January 1958. Many had been delivered to China in knocked-down form for local assembly before the deterioration of Moscow-Beijing relations, and the first Chinese version, equivalent to the MiG-19S, made its initial flight in December 1961. From mid-1962 the Jian-6 became standard equipment in the Air Force of the People's Liberation Army, and it remains so today. In addition to counterparts of the MiG-19S and SF day fighters (Nato Farmer-C), China has built or developed the Jian-6A (MiG-19PF/Farmer-D) limited all-weather fighter; Jian-6B (MiG-19PM/ Farmer-D), Jian-6C, Jian-6Xin; Jianzhen-6 (similar to the MiG-19R) and Jianjiao-6. The Jian-6A has a gun and rocket armament, while the Jian-6B is armed with Alkali-type radar homing missiles. The latter has now probably been largely replaced by the Jian-6Xin (Chinese for "new"), in which the Soviet-designed Izumrud (Emerald) intake-mounted radar is replaced by a Chinese-developed airborne interception radar in a needle-shaped radome mounted centrally on the intake splitter plate. Current production day-fighter version, the Jian-6C, is distinguished externally by a relocated brake parachute in a bullet fairing at the base of the

rudder. The Jianzhen-6 reconnaissance fighter has cameras mounted in the lower forward fuselage in place of the third 30mm cannon of the fighter-bomber versions.

In the tandem two-seat Jianjiao-6 China has again produced a "UTI" conversion of the basic single-seater, although in this instance such a version did exist, albeit in very limited numbers, in the USSR. The Chinese JJ-6, although of similar concept, was however developed entirely in China and differs from the MiG-19UTI in a number of important respects. Unlike the Soviet two-seater, in which the additional cockpit was accommodated within the existing fuselage by removing some of the fuel tanks, the JJ-6 is lengthened by 0.84m (2ft 9in) forward of the wing for this purpose. To offset the effect of this increase on the aircraft's directional stability, two ventral strakes were added underneath the rear fuselage, one on each side of the existing centreline strake. The brake chute, like that on recently produced single-seaters, is in a bullet fairing beneath the rudder. Powerplant is unchanged from that of the single-seat Jian-6, and the extra fuselage length permits an internal fuel capacity only some 170lit (37 Imp gal) less than that of the single-seater.

Production of J-6 versions was stepped up in about 1966 and several thousand have since been built, initially at Shenyang only but latterly also at Tianjin. In the Air Force of the PLA the J-6 equips more than 40 air regiments, each of which has three or four squadrons. Their duties include air-to-air interception, battlefield interdiction, close support, counter-air and tactical reconnaissance. The J-6 also serves in small numbers with the Aviation of the People's Navy. The J-6 and/or JJ-6 have been exported to Pakistan (140,

124

known as the F-6 and FT-6 respectively), Albania, Bangladesh, Egypt, Iran (via North Korea), Iraq (via Egypt and Jordan), Kampuchea, Tanzania and Vietnam. Pakistani F-6s, which equip nine air-defence and ground-attack squadrons, are fitted with rails for an AIM-9B Sidewinder air-to-air missile under each wing, and are currently being modified to carry a locally produced underbelly auxiliary fuel tank.

Combined Shenyang/Tianjin production of J-6 versions was reported in 1981 to total about 60 per month. This may however be an indication of capability rather than actual current output, at least part of which probably consists of older aircraft being refurbished or remanufactured to current standards to provide domestic replacements and to meet possible export orders. The indications are that output of older fighters is now diminishing, with increasing emphasis being placed on the development of new aircraft benefiting from China's increasing technological capability. Aircraft exports are also assuming increasing importance in the development of the Chinese economy. During the period of the fifth five-year-plan (1976-80), China exported 280 supersonic combat aircraft (presumably J/JJ-6s), five subsonic combat aircraft, ten helicopters and 180 other aircraft.

The Chinese aircraft of which details are most eagerly awaited is undoubtedly the Shenyang J-8 (Nato Finback), the subject of an advanced fighter programme begun in the early 1970s. Latest reports appear to confirm that the Jian-8 is a delta-wing aircraft larger than the Jian-7 and with vertical tail surfaces similar to those of the Mirage 2000. It also incorporates technology gleaned from the Soviet MiG-23 variable-geometry combat aircraft, one or more examples of which were received from Egypt in 1976. A prototype was seen by visiting US Defence Department and aerospace industry officials in September 1980, at which time it was described as a Mach 2 aircraft powered by a Tumansky R-11 (Chengdu Wopen-7) turbojet. However, this powerplant is regarded as being less efficient than the MiG-23's R-29, and a July 1981 report by the US Defence Intelligence Agency claimed that the J-8 had not then entered production "because the Chinese have not yet produced adequate jet engines to power the aircraft". An alternative could be the less powerful Rolls-Royce Spey 202, which China has a licence to manufacture (the first Chinese-built Spey completed a 150-hour acceptance test at Derby in the spring of 1980). But the DIA report also stated that "even with this influx of engine technology, the Chinese will require a number of years to incorporate this information into the aircraft industry".

Harbin

Harbin's earlier products included the Czechoslovak Super Aero 45 two/three-passenger twin-engined utility aircraft and the Heilongjiang No 1, an agricultural/ utility aircraft resembling the Soviet Yak-12. It is currently building the Soviet Ilyushin Il-28 tactical light bomber and the nationally designed Yun-11/12 agricultural/utility light twins. Harbin is also the chief centre

The general-purpose Yun-11 is an indigenous design, produced at Harbin in the late 1970s. Illustrated is a Y-11 in agricultural spraying configuration. A scaled-up version, with Canadian turboprops instead of Chinese-built radial engines, is scheduled for production as the Yun-12.

Left: **A group of Zhi-5 (Mil Mi-4) helicopters of the Air Force of the People's Liberation Army.** (*Air et Cosmos*)

Below: **Most recent helicopter to be produced in China is the Aérospatiale Dauphin 2, assembled under licence at Harbin as the Zhi-9.**

for helicopter production, which began with the Mil Mi-4 (Chinese designation Zhi-5), and is now developing a new helicopter known as the Zhi-6. It is also responsible for the Aérospatiale Dauphin 2 (Zhi-9) assembly programme and is sharing production of the Mil Mi-8 with the factory at Nanchang.

Some 300 Hong-5s (Chinese Il-28s) equip about a dozen air regiments of the People's Liberation Army, with about 100 more in service with the Aviation of the People's Navy. According to the US FY 1981 military

posture statement, the Hong-5 was then still in production in China; a few may be configured for nuclear weapon delivery.

Several thousand Il-28s were built in the USSR and Czechoslovakia, and about 500 of these were supplied to China, where the type entered production after the political break with the Soviet Union. Known Chinese versions are the Hong-5 standard three-seat tactical light bomber, similar to the basic Il-28 and including a torpedo-bomber version comparable with the Soviet

Il-28T; the Hongjiao-5 two-seat operational and pilot training version, similar to the Il-28U; and the Hongzhen-5 three-seat tactical reconnaissance version, similar to the Il-28R.

First details of the Chinese-designed and developed Yun-11 utility aircraft emerged in 1977, when construction of a small pre-production batch of about 15 aircraft began. The prototype is believed to have flown for the first time in 1975. These early Yun-11s were used in top-dressing and pest control operations in 1977-78; the Yun-11 is now used primarily in agricultural, forestry and geophysical survey applications. Powered by two 213kW (285hp) Huosai-6A (Quzhou-built development of the Ivchenko-Vedeneev AI-14RF) nine-cylinder radial engines, the Yun-11 normally carries a crew of two and seven passengers (with a removable folding jump-seat for an eighth passenger), or equivalent cargo.

Studies to improve the payload/range capabilities of the Y-11 resulted in the completion of three Yun-11T1 development aircraft (one for structure/static testing and two for flight test) powered by 373kW (500shp) Pratt & Whitney Aircraft of Canada PT6A-11 turboprops. First flight took place at Harbin on July 14, 1982. The additional engine power available permitted the basic Y-11 airframe to be scaled up. The principal enlargement affects the fuselage, which is extended in all three dimensions to accommodate up to 17 passengers in a commuter configuration or 14 parachutists. In addition to being slightly greater in span the wings have a new aerofoil section and incorporate additional fuel tanks. The two flying Yun-11T1s will eventually be modified for geological survey work in China; the second batch of three aircraft, designated Yun-11T2, will have 462kW (620shp) PT6A-27 engines, as will the Y-12 production version. The turboprop version is marketed outside China under the name Turbo Panda.

Harbin's first helicopter was the Zhi-5 military version of the Mil Mi-4, some 300-350 of which are estimated to remain in service with the Air Force of the PLA. A further 50 or so serve with the Aviation of the People's Navy for anti-submarine and search and rescue duties. The civil version of the Mi-4/Zhi-5 is known in China as the Xuanfeng (Whirlwind). Combined military and civil production, which began in 1959 and ended in 1979, is thought to have totalled about 1,000. The Zhi-5's Shvetsov ASh-82V engine, also built at Harbin, has the Chinese name Huosai-5A.

First indication of the existence of a Zhi-6 was given in early 1980, when a component was displayed at a trade exhibition in Shanghai. The Zhi-6 is understood to be powered by the 1,790kW (2,400shp) Wozhou-5 turboshaft, produced at Shanghai and developed from the Wojiang-5 Chinese version of the Ivchenko AI-24 turboprop. On July 2, 1980, China signed a licence agreement covering assembly at Harbin of the twin-turboshaft Aérospatiale Dauphin 2 (Haitun in Chinese)

and its Turboméca Arriel engines. Fifty Dauphins will be built initially, most of them for offshore oil rig support. The first one flew in China on February 6, 1982. Its Chinese designation is Zhi-9, leaving open to speculation the identities of the Zhi-7 and Zhi-8. One of these is almost certainly the Mil Mi-8, components for which are being produced at both Harbin and Nanchang.

Nanchang

Nanchang, previously responsible for licence production of the Soviet Yak-18A basic trainer (Chinese designation Chujiao-5), is currently manufacturing its own development of this aircraft (the Chujiao-6), and the Qiang-5 attack aircraft developed from the Jian-6/MiG-19.

Despite a close similarity to the Yak-18A the tandem-seat CJ-6 is essentially an indigenous redesign, and was developed to replace the CJ-5. Powered by a 213kW (285hp) Huosai-6A, it is reported to have been in production since 1961. More than 2,000 have been delivered, including exports to Bangladesh, Korea, Vietnam and Zambia.

The Qiang-5 twin-engined fighter-bomber is based substantially on the airframe of the Jian-6, but with overall dimensions slightly increased. The wings are basically unchanged, but to make room for an internal weapons bay it was decided to transfer equipment from the centre fuselage to a solid ogival nose and to provide lateral engine air intakes abreast of the single-seat cockpit. The cockpit canopy differs from that of the J-6 in being hinged at the rear to open upwards, with a deeper spine fairing behind it. The J-6 powerplant of two Shenyang Wopen-6 turbojet engines (Tumansky/Mikulin R-9BF) remains basically unchanged. There is significant area-rule waisting of the central portion of the fuselage. The taller main fin has a smaller dorsal extension than that of the J-6, and there are shorter twin strakes below the tail. Horizontal tail surfaces are similar to those of the J-6. There is a brake parachute housed in the tailcone of early production Q-5s; on later aircraft, as on recently built J-6s, this is relocated in a bullet fairing below the rudder.

Like the J-6, the Q-5 has two wing-mounted cannon. These occupy the revised wing-root position outboard of the intake trunks and are believed to be of 23mm calibre. Underwing stores normally comprise two 760lit (167 Imp gal) drop-tanks on the outboard pylons and two pods of air-to-surface rockets (57mm Soviet S-5 or Chinese 90mm) or two 250kg bombs on the inboard pylons. The internal bay, capable of housing four 250kg bombs, is located aft of the underfuselage airbrake, and there is an external attachment each side of this bay for two more 250kg bombs. A single 5-20KT nuclear bomb can be carried.

According to one report, at least 210 Qiang-5s were in service with tactical strike fighter squadrons of the

PLA by 1979, and a 1980 report claimed that the aircraft had been built in "relatively large numbers". The Q-5 serves also in an air-defence role with the People's Navy, and deliveries of 42 to the Pakistani Air Force began in 1982.

Nanchang was also the original production centre for the Yun-5 (Antonov An-2) general-purpose biplane.

Top: **Two of the types built most extensively by the Chinese aerospace industry are the Yun-5 (An-2) general-purpose biplane and, nearer the camera, the Nanchang Chujiao-6 piston-engined basic trainer.**

Above: **First front-line combat aircraft to be designed in China, the Qiang-5 (Nato Fantan-A) is a derivative of the Jian-6/MiG-19.**

The An-2 was supplied to China and since 1957 has been built under licence in large numbers (more than 1,000). Its 746kW (1,000hp) Shvetsov ASh-62IR engine, built at Quzhou, has the Chinese name Huosai-5. The Y-5 continues to be used extensively both by the Air Force, which has several hundred, and in a civil capacity, for agricultural and general transport work, by Chinese state airline CAAC. Production was moved in later years to Harbin, and more recently was reported to be continuing (probably at a reduced rate) at Shijiazhuang.

Xian

Aircraft built at the Xian works include the Tupolev Tu-16 bomber (Chinese designation Hong-6), Chinese versions of the Mikoyan MiG-21 fighter (Jian-7), and the Antonov An-24 transport (as the Yun-7). Xian also produces Wopen-8 (RD-3M) jet engines for the Tu-16/H-6, and is the centre for licence production of the Rolls-Royce Spey 202 turbofan.

First steps to assemble the Tu-16 under licence in China were taken in 1958, but work was suspended in 1960 after the political break with the USSR. A production programme was reinstated some two years later, and the formidable task of copying the design without Soviet assistance was undertaken. Deliveries of the Chinese-built Hong-6 version began in about 1968, and seven of the 26 nuclear devices tested at Lop Nor up to

1980 were dropped from Tu-16/H-6s. Though production of this aircraft has been relatively slow, recent US military posture statements have confirmed that it is continuing, and the number in service is now believed to be about 100. China is also supplying spares for the Tu-16 bombers of the Egyptian Air Force, and the possibility remains that China may develop ECM, reconnaissance, tanker or other variants at some future date.

Design of a Chinese copy of the MiG-21 was based on data gleaned from a number of Soviet-built MiG-21Fs (Nato Fishbed-C) delivered to China before the political break. In contrast to the Tu-16/H-6 programme, the task of copying the airframe, the R-11 afterburning turbojet (built at Chengdu as the Wopen-7) and equipment was completed much more quickly, and the Jian-7 made its first flight in December 1964. It began to enter service with the PLA Air Force in 1965. Production was then halted in 1966 after some 60-80 had been completed, but has been resumed in recent years, possibly with engine, cockpit and avionics changes. A reconnaissance version is also said to have been

---

Final-assembly line at Xian for the Hong-6 (Tu-16) medium bomber, about 100 of which are in service with the PLA Air Force. (*Liu Zhibin*)

Xian Jian-7s, Chinese-built counterparts of the MiG-21F. (*Zhou Yi*)

developed. The MiG-21/Jian-7 is currently thought to equip two or three air regiments of the PLA; others have been exported to Albania and Tanzania. Components and engines have been exported in some numbers to Egypt, which has also ordered up to 100 Jian-7s for its own use (as advanced trainers) and for supply to Iraq.

Civil and military examples of the Antonov An-24 twin-turboprop transport aircraft have been in service with CAAC and the PLA Air Force since about 1970. Soviet manufacture of this 48/52-passenger aircraft ended in 1978, but it is currently in production at Xian (as the Yun-7) following the completion during recent years of nine pre-series aircraft. The aircraft's 1,901kW (2,550ehp) Ivchenko AI-24A engines are manufactured at Shanghai under the Chinese designation Wojiang-5A-1. Public debut of one of the pre-production Y-7s took place on April 17, 1982, at Nanyuan Airport, Beijing, and production was due to begin during that year, initially to replace Soviet-built Il-14s and Il-18s in service with CAAC.

Hanzhong

With its enormous numbers of ground troops, China is notably short of medium and heavy airlift capability. It did not therefore come as too much of a surprise when about two years ago it was learned that the industry was building its own version of the Antonov An-12BP four-turboprop civil/military transport aircraft (Chinese designation Yun-8). Like the smaller An-24, the An-12 has been in service with both the country's military services and the state airline for several years, though in small numbers. The aircraft's 2,983kW (4,000ehp) Ivchenko AI-20K engines are produced at Shanghai under the Chinese designation Wojiang-6.

Production of the Yun-8 (An-12BP copy) at Hanzhong could help to provide China's air forces with a much needed improvement in airlift capability.

Shanghai

World attention was focused on the Shanghai factory when, on December 8, 1981, the prototype of China's Yun-10 four-jet transport made its public debut with a 1hr 48min flight from Shanghai to Beijing carrying "several dozen" passengers. In fact, in addition to the flight crew of five, there is room in the air-conditioned and pressurised main cabin for up to 178 passengers in a six-abreast layout. More typical layouts could provide for 124-passenger (mixed-class, international flights), 149-passenger (single-class, domestic flights), mixed passenger/cargo and all-cargo configurations.

The programme to produce the first jet airliner of Chinese design and manufacture began in about 1970. Although the Yun-10 is very similar in configuration to the Boeing 707, its design was in fact initiated some two years before the first 707-320s were delivered to China. The Yun-10 has four 84.5kN (19,000lb st) Pratt & Whitney JT3D-7 turbofans, which are available in China in the form of spares for the 707-320 fleet. The aircraft's seating capacity approximates more closely to that of the smaller 707-120B, although the fuselage and cabin are shorter and the wing span is greater. Three prototypes of the Y-10 have been built, of which the first was used at Xian in the late 1970s for static load testing and the third was allocated to major subassembly tests. First flight, by the No 2 aircraft, was made on September 26, 1980.

Design and manufacture of the Yun-10 were ostensibly undertaken primarily to demonstrate the Chinese industry's ability to develop an aircraft of this type. However, as the Chinese press has pointed out, it possesses development potential as an aeromedical transport (110 stretchers and seven medical personnel), freighter (up to 12 containers or seven jeeps), troop transport (160 seats), or Awacs-type airborne early-warning aircraft. An Awacs version powered by two CFM56 turbofans is said to be under study.

Many of the foregoing programmes demonstrate the

The prototype Shanghai Yun-10, first jet airliner of Chinese design and manufacture, which flew for the first time in 1980.

determination and ability of the Chinese to get themselves out of difficult situations as far as possible by their own efforts. The policy of the present leadership is to make China a modern, independent, developed world power by the year 2000 under its "four modernisations" programme, for agriculture, industry, defence, and science and technology. However, they have recognised that there is not enough time to achieve this goal totally unaided, and have shown an increasing willingness to acquire Western technology while continuing to encourage and develop the potential talents available at home.

Meanwhile, by its own standards the country has accomplished much in the past dozen or so years. The condescending Western term "Chinese copy" takes on a very different meaning when applied to an industry which can develop its own nuclear weapons, launch vehicles and communications satellites, or dissect, analyse and put into production complex combat aircraft and modern gas-turbine engines. Productivity is low by Western standards, it is true, and a lack of automation means that the aerospace industry is heavily labour-intensive. But, seen in Chinese terms, this is perhaps less worrying than it would be elsewhere, given the enormous population which must be kept in work. Progress in defence and industry modernisation has so far benefited the Navy more than the other armed forces, and too much of China's military aircraft and avionics production still reflects 1960s technology. Nevertheless, in spite of weak foundations and a relatively short history the Chinese aerospace industry has come a long way in the past decade and a half — and there are still 17 years to go before the end of the century.

Thunderbirds fly Falcons

Michael J. H. Taylor

F-16 FIGHTING FALCON

As they begin their 31st year of existence, the USAF Thunderbirds will continue the tradition of excellence established by their compatriots of years past. The transition to the General Dynamics F-16 Fighting Falcon brings a new operational concept for the team. With the F-16, the Thunderbirds are flying a combat aircraft that is representative of the Air Force mission and its capabilities.

Flying the "Fighting Falcon" allows the team to perform the air demonstration role while it maintains full combat capability. Although the aircraft are painted in the traditional red, white, and blue colors of the Thunderbirds, the F-16s have no modifications that affect the combat capability of the aircraft. The Thunderbirds' F-16s can be repainted and restored to combat configuration within 72 hours.

The F-16 is a multinational fighter aircraft in use around the world by the USAF and many of our allies. Advanced aerodynamics, combined with a high thrust-to-weight ratio, make the F-16 more maneuverable than any other fighter in the world today. The F-16's outstanding performance will enable the Thunderbirds to perform at a level that has not been possible in previous aircraft.

UNITED STATES AIR FORCE · USAF

Below: **The Thunderbirds flying their newly acquired F-16 Fighting Falcons.** (USAF)

This year sees the 30th anniversary of the first display by the Thunderbirds, the US Air Force's official air demonstration squadron. In three decades the squadron has thrilled onlookers in the USA and 45 other countries, logging 2,455 performances in front of an estimated total of 155 million people.

The Thunderbirds first took to the air in Republic F-84G Thunderjets, moving to F-84F Thunderstreaks in 1955 and North American F-100C Super Sabres, their first supersonic mounts, in 1956. In 1964 the F-100Cs were superseded by Republic F-105B Thunderchiefs, but only six official demonstrations were flown before the squadron switched to the F-100D. Indeed, the Thunderbirds did more time on the "Hun" than on any other aircraft, and retained the North American type for a further five seasons. The total number of performances with the F-100C/D had reached 1,111 by 1969, when the team got McDonnell Douglas F-4E Phantom IIs.

In 1974 the Thunderbirds received Northrop T-38A Talon supersonic trainers, retaining these until this 31st season, when they proudly flew into a new era of aircraft technology with their eighth jet type, the General Dynamics F-16 Fighting Falcon.

Too many trainers?

Kenneth Munson

At a rough count there are about 150 nations which have an air arm of some kind or another. Whatever their size and sophistication, they all have one need in common: training for their pilots. Seldom can there have been such a wide selection of training aircraft from which to choose. About 50 different specialised trainers are currently available or under development, without counting the many two-seat variants of combat aircraft, off-the-shelf civil types, licence programmes such as those resulting in Brazilian-built Italian MB.326s and Israeli-built French Fougas, or helicopters.

At first sight this embarrassment of riches appears to be a self-indulgence which air forces and aircraft industries in a recession-hit world can ill afford. One eminent aviation weekly earlier this year declared it "absurd for so many manufactures to pour vast sums into so many trainers with little difference between them," arguing that in what is essentially a buyer's market it would pay air forces to get together in groups to select a design to meet their broadly common requirements.

It is not difficult to see the merits of such an argument. Some estimates have put the market for new training aircraft during the remainder of the 1980s at 3,000 aircraft. Individual air forces are seldom likely to require more than 100-150 each, and only about half of the 50 trainers currently on offer can boast orders for that many. On the other hand, a combined order for up to 400 of a single mutually acceptable type from (say) the Royal Air Force, the Royal Australian Air Force and the Canadian Armed Forces could reduce the unit

Argentina's Fabrica Militar de Aviones received technical assistance from Dornier with the design of its IA 63 basic/advanced trainer, which helps to explain an external resemblance to the larger Alpha Jet. This mock-up was shown at the 1981 Paris Show; the first prototype was due to fly in late 1983.

Above: **One of the most attractive new-generation trainers is the turboprop Tucano (Toucan) from Embraer of Brazil. Created only 14 years ago, this go-ahead company has built some 3,000 military and civil aircraft and is recognised as one of the world's leading aerospace manufacturers.** (Embraer)

Below: **Although outwardly very similar to the long-serving Soviet Yak-18A, China's Nanchang CJ-6 was much redesigned by Chinese engineers to suit different national requirements. It has been in production for some 20 years and examples have been exported to Bangladesh, North Korea, Vietnam and Zambia.**

Used by all Warsaw Pact countries except Poland, the L-39 Albatros (well over 1,000 built already) has proved a worthy successor to Aero's L-29 Delfin. Major customer for this Czech design is the USSR; others include Afghanistan, Angola, Benin, Congo, Ethiopia, East Germany, Guinea-Bissau, Iraq, Libya, Madagascar, Mozambique, Sao Tome/Principe, South Yemen and Tanzania.

cost of the chosen trainer to a level that would leave most of its competitors standing. Lower unit costs could also help to alleviate a major training problem. The dwindling world fuel supply and constantly rising defence costs mean that training programmes receive less funding priority than they deserve, and a number of air forces are combating this by revamping the training syllabus to include more hours in the simulator and fewer in the air. Others, like France's Armée de l'Air, have decided that they can maintain both the efficiency and the cost-effectiveness of their flying training programmes by using in the early stages propeller-driven aircraft like the new Epsilon instead of jets such as the long-serving Magister.

In an ideal world it might indeed make sense for nations to band together in choosing a single type of trainer to meet their collective needs. The real world, however, is divided by conflicting ideologies, the supposed need for national prestige, and the unquestionable need for national economies to remain at least viable and preferably profitable. International design part-

Below: **Aérospatiale's piston-powered Epsilon, designed by the company's Socata light aircraft subsidiary, looks as though it ought to be a turboprop. The French Air Force, which wants 150, decided that switching to a propeller-driven aircraft would make its ab initio pilot training more cost-effective.** (*Aérospatiale*)

Left: **One of the smallest jet trainers at present under development is the V-tailed Microjet 200. Designed by Microturbo to help in promoting its range of small jet engines, it is also intended to appeal to customers by virtue of its low initial and operating costs.** (*Gifas*)

Centre left: **Perhaps the least orthodox of all currently available trainers, the German RFB Fantrainer has a turboshaft powerplant driving a five-blade ducted fan. Development has been somewhat protracted but was rewarded in 1982 with an order for 47 from the Royal Thai Air Force.**

Below: **One of the most up-market performers is the Franco-German Alpha Jet, 175 of which serve with each of the two parent air forces. Despite its sophistication and price, it has also secured orders totalling nearly 150 aircraft from smaller air forces such as those of Cameroun, Egypt, Ivory Coast, Morocco, Nigeria, Qatar and Togo.** (*Dassault-Breguet*)

Above: **Relying extensively on the design and successful operating record of the earlier MB.326, Aermacchi's MB.339A equips not only Italian Air Force flying training schools but also the national aerobatic team, the** *Frecce Tricolori*. **First foreign customer is Peru, which is to build 66 (including single-seat MB.339Ks) under licence.**

nerships can work, and work well, as evidenced by the no fewer than 13 such programmes listed in the current pages of *Jane's All the World's Aircraft*. But it is no accident that only one of these programmes concerns a training aircraft (the Alpha Jet), and even that is really a multi-role aircraft rather than a pure trainer.

The reasons are not hard to detect. Combat and large transport aircraft are often too expensive or too complex for single companies or nations to launch on their own, while small and uncomplicated aircraft like trainers are not. Often, as in the case of Finland's Vinka/Miltrainer, they may be the only affordable means (other than subcontract work) of keeping a long-established company or national aircraft industry alive. In other countries, such as Peru and Chile in recent years, they can provide an ideal subject on which a newly established national industry can cut its teeth. It needs only a glance at neighbouring Brazil to appreciate what that can lead to within a comparatively short space of time. That is why, to return to the earlier example, it is most unlikely that Australia will join with the RAF or anyone else in choosing a foreign trainer for the RAAF: its own industry has too much need of a home-grown programme.

There is of course another side to this coin. As more national industries develop more national trainers, so they reduce the potential export market for the products of the larger companies and nations. It is difficult to see Italy, for example, succeeding commercially with all five of the trainers it currently has on offer, or Switzerland's AS 32T making much impact when the Pilatus PC-7 has already done so well. Perhaps the best way out of this dilemma is that adopted by Casa of Spain, which, while licensing its own C-101 advanced jet trainer for production in Chile, is at the same time trying to persuade the Spanish Air Force to adopt Chile's piston-engined Pillan for the ab initio part of the training syllabus.

137

Of the 50 or so piston, turboprop and jet-engined trainers which at present make up the shopping list, nearly 20 are still in the development/flight test/certification stages, and it would perhaps be unfair to pre-judge their chances of attracting substantial orders. Some, like the USAF's Fairchild T-46A (650 needed) and Japan's XT-4 (up to 200 required), seem set to fare well. Equally certainly, a proportion of the others will not. Of the remaining 30-plus types already in production — some of them for many years — only a dozen or so can boast order books of 200 or more. Too many trainers? It certainly looks that way.

Right: **While other Warsaw Pact nations standardised on the Czech L-29 and L-39, Poland decided to go it alone with PZL-Mielec's TS-11 Iskra. Production for the Polish Air Force has exceeded 500, and 50 were sold to India. An improved Iskra 2 is now under development.** (*PZL-Mielec*)

Left: **Although it has a decade of experience in building turbine-powered helicopters, the Romanian industry has turned only recently to fixed-wing turboprop aircraft. Most recent of these is ICA Brasov's IAR-825TP Triumf, first seen publicly at last year's Farnborough Show.**

Left: **Few piston-engined trainers have enjoyed such worldwide popularity as the Siai-Marchetti SF.260. More than 800 examples of this Stelio Frati design have been sold to over a score of air forces, large and small. A turboprop version became available in 1982. This SF.260MC serves with the air force of Zaîre.**

Right: **Casa of Spain has secured a Chilean export order for its C-101 Aviojet, some of which will be built under licence in that country. In return, Casa is promoting Chile's piston-engined Pillan to fill a Spanish Air Force requirement.**

Left: **The Pilatus PC-7 Turbo-Trainer provides proof that substantial home orders are not necessarily required before a good design can succeed abroad. More than 150 had been sold worldwide before the Swiss Air Force bought 40, and total sales are now in the region of 300.** (*Pilatus*)

Right: **US recognition of the Chinese People's Republic increased Taiwan's need to develop an independent aircraft industry. Its links with the US industry remain strong, and AIDC's AT-TC-3 was designed with Northrop assistance. Northrop also helped with Spain's Casa C-101.**

Above: **Most successful Western jet trainer in production today is the British Aerospace Hawk, which in late 1981 was selected against strong US and foreign competition to meet the US Navy's 307-aircraft VTX-TS requirement.** (BAe)

Right: **The original piston-engined Beechcraft T-34 entered production as long ago as 1953, and the turbine-powered T-34C appeared 20 years later. Despite its age this popular aircraft is still attracting home and overseas orders; the US Navy began to receive 120 new T-34Cs this year and plans to order more. Foreign operators include Algeria, Argentina, Ecuador, Gabon, Indonesia, Morocco, Peru and Uruguay.** (Beech)

Right: **It is more than 20 years since the prototype Galeb first flew. With the single-seat Jastreb ground-attack version, it has been a standard Yugoslav Air Force type ever since, as well as being exported to Libya and Zambia. In 1981 Soko flew the G4 Super Galeb (illustrated), a swept-wing derivative very similar in appearance to the BAe Hawk.** (Austin J. Brown)

Jarrett's jubilees

Philip Jarrett

75 years ago

1908 was a year of great achievements in the new art of flying, and heralded the aeroplane's advent as a practical vehicle. The year began with the first officially observed circular 1km flight in Europe, accomplished by Henri Farman in his modified Voisin-Farman I at Issy on January 13. This won Farman a Deutsch-Archdeacon prize of Fr50,000. The 1min 28sec flight necessitated wide, yawing turns, such was the aeroplane's lack of lateral control.

On May 29, in the same biplane further modified, Farman took Ernest Archdeacon for an 11sec, 131m (430ft) flight at Ghent. It was the first passenger-carrying flight in Europe and was followed on July 6 by the first flight by a European to exceed 15min duration, for which Farman won another Fr10,000.

On June 28 at Kiel the Dane Jacob Ellehammer made the first official hop flight in Germany in his No

Glenn Curtiss in the cockpit of AEA *Red Wing.* (*National Museums of Canada*)

AEA *White Wing.* (*Canadian National Museum of Science & Technology*)

Curtiss flying AEA *June Bug*, **winner of the** *Scientific American* **trophy.** *(National Museums of Canada)*

IV tractor biplane. In Canada Dr Graham Bell's Aerial Experiment Association (AEA) tested its first powered machine on ice-covered Lake Keuka on March 12. This was the ski-equipped *Red Wing* pusher biplane. After a crash landing on its second hop, this aircraft was succeeded by *White Wing*, which made five take-offs from May 18 to 23, covering 310m (1,017ft) in 19sec on May 22. *June Bug*, the AEA's third powered aeroplane, was designed by Glenn Curtiss. Though still primitive it was a much more practical machine than its predecessors and made many take-offs between June 21 and August 31, usually flown by its designer or by J. A. D. McCurdy. On July 4 Curtiss made a flight of 1,551m (5,090ft) in 1min 42.5sec to win the *Scientific American* trophy for the first officially recorded flight of more than 1km (0.6mile) in the USA.

In France both Robert Esnault-Pelterie and Louis Blériot were experimenting with improved monoplanes, the Blériot VIII being a reasonably successful machine approaching the classic monoplane form. The foremost aeroplane of 1908, however, was not French but the latest *Flyer* of Wilbur and Orville Wright. When flown by Wilbur in France from August it astounded the European experimenters with its man-

Blériot VIII.

Lt Selfridge and Orville Wright at Fort Myer, September 1908. (*Smithsonian Institution*)

Wright *Flyer* **in France in 1908.**

Top: **Henri Farman inspects his I-*bis* biplane.**

Above: **Gastambide-Mengin monoplane.** (*Science Museum*)

oeuvrability and controllability, though it had to be "flown" all the time and lacked the inherent stability of its European counterparts. In all, some 26hr in the air in the course of 104 flights were logged by the end of the year.

Preparations for these momentous efforts had included the world's first two passenger flights, on May 14, when both brothers had taken up C. W. Furnas at Kill Devil Hills in their 1905 *Flyer III*. While Wilbur took Europe by storm, Orville was flying a similar machine at Fort Myer in the USA in US Signal Corps tests of the Wrights' ability to meet US Army specifications. Though successful, these trials were

marred by the first fatal crash of a powered aircraft when, on September 17, a cracked propeller blade caused the aircraft to dive into the ground. Orville's passenger, Lt Selfridge (one of the AEA team), was killed and Orville sustained serious injuries but recovered.

While the Wrights' 1908 flights far surpassed those of the Europeans, Farman and Leon Delagrange steadily improved as the year drew to a close. After fitting ailerons to his I-*bis* biplane, Farman made the world's first proper cross-country flight, from Buoy to Reims on October 30, covering 27km (16.7 miles) in 20min.

Late 1908 saw Britain's first real success in heavier-than-air powered flight. On October 16 the expatriate American S. F. Cody made what is now recognised as the first powered flight in Britain, at Farnborough in Hampshire. His biplane, British Army Aeroplane No 1, was the result of work with kites and displayed strong Wright influence. Its 37.3kW (50hp) Antoinette engine drove two pusher propellers.

In February the Gastambide-Mengin monoplane had appeared in France. It had not been successful, making only one reasonable flight (on August 21) after many alterations. But its offspring, the celebrated Antoinette monoplanes, made their debut in October. The Antoinette IV first flew on October 9 but really notable flights wouldn't come until the new year. The Antoinette V flew on December 20. Also waiting to make its flying debut in 1909 was Blériot's No XI monoplane, which was displayed at the Salon de l'Automobile in Paris during the last week of December.

The climax to 1908 came on the last day of the year, when Wilbur Wright made a flight of 124km (77 miles) in 2hr 20min at Camp d'Auvours. This won him the Michelin prize of Fr20,000, less than half the amount won by Farman at the start of the year for a flight 124th as far!

50 years ago

1933 began well for Britain, which captured the world record for distance in a straight line. This flight began on February 6 at 7.15 a.m, when Sqn Ldr O. R. Gayford and Flt Lt G. E. Nicholetts took off from RAF Cranwell in Fairey Long-range Monoplane K1991 and set course for Africa. The aircraft, weighing 7,938kg (17,500lb) gross, made a 1,372m (4,500ft) take-off run. At 4.40 p.m on February 8, after 57hr 25min in the air, the aeroplane touched down at Walvis Bay, Southwest Africa. The flight had been comparatively trouble-free though the autopilot had failed south of Nigeria, and a non-stop distance of 8,544km (5,309 miles) had been covered. Britain now held the absolute world records for distance, altitude and speed. A new Napier Lion engine was installed following a 7hr flight to Cape Town, and the Monoplane flew back to England, landing at Farnborough on May 2.

The same day that K1991 left Cranwell, Jim Mollison flew out of Lympne in Puss Moth G-ABXY *The Heart's Content*. Three days 10hr 8min later he touched down at Port Natal, Brazil, having covered 7,403km (4,600 miles). He had made the first solo east-west crossing of the South Atlantic, achieved in a record time of 17hr 40min.

On February 18 Imperial Airways notched up its first ten million miles of flying. Britain had still more to celebrate on April 3 when two Westland biplanes (P.V.3 G-ACAZ flown by Sqn Ldr the Marquis of Clydesdale, accompanied by cinematographer L. V. S. Blacker, and P.V.6 G-ACBR carrying pilot Flt Lt D. F. McIntyre and S. R. Bonnet) made the first flight over Mount Everest. The summit was cleared by 30.5m (100ft). A second flight followed on April 19.

Disaster struck on April 4 when the American rigid airship *Akron* was lost during US Navy fleet manoeuvres after her tail struck the water, precipitating a

Fairey Long-range Monoplane K1991.

Above: **Westland P.V.3 G-ACAZ**, one of the two aircraft which made the first flight over **Mount Everest**. *(Westland)*

Below: **Italian Macchi M.C.72 racing seaplane, fitted with contra-rotating propellers.** *(Flight International)*

Above: **Cyclone-powered Lockheed Sirius seaplane flown by Charles and Ann Lindbergh.**

structural breakup. Only three of the 76 men aboard survived.

On April 10 Britain lost the world absolute speed record when Warrant Officer Francesco Agello of Italy reached 682.078km/hr (423.822mph) in his Macchi M.C.72 racing seaplane over Lago di Garda. The M.C.72's powerplant was a Fiat AS.6 24-cylinder piston engine of 2,088kW (2,800hp), essentially a pair of 12-cylinder AS.5s mounted in tandem and driving contra-rotating propellers.

July 1 saw the maiden flight of the Douglas DC-1 airliner at Clover Field, Santa Monica, California. Progenitor of the most famous transport aeroplane of all time, the DC-3, the sole DC-1 was to survive until December 1940.

That same day an amazing double crossing of the Atlantic began. A wing of two squadrons of Italian Savoia-Marchetti S-55X flying boats (a total of 24 aircraft crewed by more than 100 officers and men led by General Italo Balbo, the Italian Air Minister) made the flight in stages, crossing the Apennines and Alps and stopping at Londonderry, Reykjavik, Cartwright on the Labrador coast, Montreal and finally Chicago. The return flight began on July 25 and was made via the Azores. The aircraft arrived home on August 12, having covered more than 19,000km (12,000 miles) in 43 days. Two accidents had marred the flight, which meant that a reserve aircraft was among the 23 that completed the epic journey. The collective noun "bal-

bo" was used for many years afterwards to describe a large formation of aircraft.

On July 9 Col Charles A. Lindbergh and his wife Ann, flying a Cyclone-powered Lockheed Sirius seaplane, set off on a 46,600km (29,000-mile) survey flight from New York to Labrador, Greenland, Iceland, Europe, the Azores, Africa, Brazil and back. They were not to return until December 19.

On July 15 one-eyed American record-breaker Wiley Post took off in Lockheed Vega *Winnie Mae* from Floyd Bennett Field, New York, at the start of the first solo round-the-world flight. Passing through Berlin, Moscow, Irkutsk and Alaska, the 25,099km (15,596-mile) flight was completed on July 22.

The day that Post completed his flight, Amy and Jim Mollison left Pendine Sands, Wales, in their D.H.84 Dragon *Seafarer* on a second attempt to fly to New York, whence an attack on the world long-distance record would be made. After 39hr in the air headwinds forced a premature landing at Bridgeport, Connecticut, on July 24, in which the aircraft was wrecked.

The straight-line distance record claimed by Britain at the start of the year was taken for France by Paul Codos and Maurice Rossi in August. Their flight from New York to a French aerodrome at Rayak, Syria, in Blériot 110 *Joseph Le Brix* began on August 5 and was completed two days later. It covered 9,104.700km (5,657.387 miles) at an average speed of 102 mph.

Another record fell on September 4, when American James R. Weddell pushed his Weddell-Williams 44 racing monoplane to 490.686km/hr (304.521mph), taking the world speed record for landplanes. Later that month, on September 28, Britain lost the last of its three absolute world records when Gustave Lemoine

took off in the Potez 506 biplane from Villacoublay and reached 13,661m (44,819ft) to set a new world altitude record for France.

October 4 saw the departure of Sir Charles Kingsford Smith from Lympne, England, on a solo flight to Australia, flying Percival Gull Four G-ACJV *Miss Southern Cross*. He landed at Wyndham 16,000km (10,000 miles) and 7 days 4hr 4min later to become the holder of the new record for the route.

Yet another speed record fell towards the end of 1933. One-legged Major Alexander P. de Seversky, in his own company's SEV-3XAR three-seat twin-float monoplane powered by a 313kW (420hp) Wright Whirlwind, reached 289.000km/hr (179.576mph) at Roosevelt Field, New York, to set a new world record for amphibians.

25 years ago

A record for distance in a straight line opened 1958. On April 8 Brig-Gen W. E. Eubank and his crew flew a Boeing KC-135 from Tokyo to Lajes in the Azores, a distance of 16,462.500km (10,229.303 miles). Then followed a curious record, for the greatest altitude from which a successful emergency escape has been made. This was claimed on April 9 by the crew of an English Electric Canberra which exploded over Monyash, Derbyshire. Flt Lt John de Salis and Fg Off Patrick Lowe fell free from 17,070m (56,000ft), where the

Top: **Amy and Jim Mollison's de Havilland Dragon,** *Seafarer.*

Above: **Brig-Gen W. E. Eubank and crew after their arrival back at McGuire AFB in the record-breaking KC-135 tanker on April 11, 1958.** (*US Air Force*)

Right: **Grumman F11F-1F Tiger.** (*Grumman*)

temperature was −56.7°C (−70°F), to 3,050m (10,000ft), when their parachutes were automatically deployed by barometric control.

On April 10 the Fairey Rotodyne transport convertiplane made its first transitions from helicopter to autogyro horizontal flight mode, with the rotor freewheeling. The transitions were made at 1,200m (4,000ft). Such was the success of this aircraft that even today the Rotodyne still holds an official world speed record for convertiplanes, that for speed in a 100km closed circuit.

On April 18 a world absolute height record was claimed for the USA by Lt-Cdr George C. Watkins of the US Navy. Flying a Grumman F11F-1F Tiger fitted with a General Electric J79-GE-3A turbojet of 66.72kN (15,000lb st) with afterburning, he reached 23,449m (76,932ft).

April 27 saw the maiden flight of the first de Havilland Comet 4 (G-APDA). Built to meet BOAC's requirements for North Atlantic services, the type had four 46.71kN (10,500lb st) Rolls-Royce Avon turbojets and greater fuel capacity than its forebears. The altitude record achieved by Lt-Cdr Watkins was to be short-lived. On May 2 France's experimental Sud-Ouest S.O.9050 Trident II single-seat mixed-power interceptor pushed it to 24,217m (79,452ft). Piloted by R. Carpentier, the Trident II was powered by a 29.42kN (6,614lb st) SEPR 631 twin-barrel rocket

Top: **de Havilland Comet 4 G-APDA**. (*Flight International*)

Above: **Rocket-powered S.O.9050 Trident II carrying an air-to-air missile under its fuselage.** (*Ouest-Aviation*)

motor in the fuselage and a 14.71kN (3,307lb st) Turboméca Gabizo turbojet at each wingtip. As well as the absolute height record, a height record for rocket aircraft was established. It was the final flight of the extraordinary Tridents before economy measures forced cancellation of the programme, which had begun in the early 1950s.

Once again, however, the altitude record was to be quickly bettered, though this had to wait its turn. First, on May 7, Capt Walter W. Irwin of the USAF's 83rd Fighter-Interceptor Squadron set a new world absolute speed record of 2,259.538km/hr (1,404.009mph) in a Lockheed YF-104A Starfighter at Edwards Air Force Base. Then, on May 16, fellow 83rd Squadron pilot Maj H. C. Johnson took the YF-104A up to 27,811m (91,243ft) from Edwards. This made the F-104 the first aeroplane ever to hold the absolute speed and height records simultaneously. They were the first of many records to fall to this amazing stub-winged fighter over the following years.

In fact May was a good month all round for new

height records by American pilots. On May 22 and 23 a production version of the US Navy's Douglas F4D-1 Skyray fighter, flown from Point Mugu by Col Edward N. LeFaivre, set no fewer than five time-to-height records: May 22, 3,000m in 44.39sec; 6,000m in 1min 6.13sec; 9,000m in 1min 29.81sec; May 23, 12,000m in 1min 51.23sec; 15,000m in 2min 36.05sec.

Two particularly interesting experimental aircraft also made news in May. On May 21 the Breguet 940 Integral short take-off and landing (Stol) research aircraft made its first flight. Powered by four 298kW (400hp) Turboméca Turmo II turboprops, it featured large-diameter three-blade propellers positioned to provide slipstream across the whole wing span. In England, on May 23, the second Short S.C.1 Vtol jet aircraft (XG905) made the first tethered hovering flights

by the type, in the hands of Tom Brooke-Smith. Power was provided by four Rolls-Royce RB.108 lift engines.

New transatlantic records were set by two Boeing KC-135 tankers of the USAF's Eighth Air Force on June 27. They left Westover Air Force Base, Massachusetts, to fly non-stop to Brize Norton in Oxfordshire, England, completing the eastbound flight in 5hr 27min 42.8sec (an average speed of 1,014.2km/hr; 630.2mph) and 5hr 29min 37sec (average speed of 1008.2km/hr; 626.5mph) to clip some 50min from the three-year-old record, held by a Canberra.

A record on a smaller scale fell to the USA on August 1 when Capt Marion Boling, a United Airlines pilot, made a non-stop flight of 11,131km (6,979 miles) in a Beechcraft Bonanza. The flight, from Manila to Pendleton, Oregon, beat the previous record of 7,977km

Breguet 940 Integral Stol research aircraft.

(4,957 miles) for a non-stop unrefuelled flight by a single-engined aircraft, established by another Bonanza in 1949.

Boeing's KC-135 entered the record books yet again on September 17. On this occasion Capt C. E. Gibbs and his crew claimed the record for speed with payload over a 5,000km closed circuit, flying at 944.907km/hr (587.137mph) with 1,000, 2,000, 5,000 and 10,000kg loads. They also took the record for distance in a closed circuit to 5,026.900km (3,123.565 miles).

Boeing aircraft continued to hold the limelight in September. On the 16th a B-52D Stratofortress long-range strategic bomber flown by USAF Capt C. Griswold and his crew took the record for speed over a 5,000km closed circuit, reaching 961.867km/hr (597.675mph). Ten days later another B-52, with Lt Col V. L. Sandaez in command, set a record over a 10,000km closed circuit of 902.369km/hr (560.705mph).

Meanwhile, on September 14 Comet 4 G-APDA had been flown by John Cunningham from Hong Kong to London, a distance of 12,754km (7,925 miles), in a flying time of 16hr 16min. Three days later the same aircraft reduced the London-Gander record to 5hr 47min. Finally, on October 4, the world's first transatlantic jet flights with farepaying passengers were carried out by BOAC Comet 4s. Simultaneous flights were made in each direction. The London-New York service was flown by G-APDC, with Capt R. E. Millichap in command, and the New York-London flight — completed in the record time of 6hr 11min — was commanded by Capt T. B. Stoney in G-APDB.

Another notable transatlantic flight occurred on October 11. An Avro Vulcan bomber of 617 Squadron, RAF, piloted by Sqn Ldr L. R. Davenport on a "Lone Ranger" sortie, flew from Goose Bay to its Waddington base in 3hr 53min. The average speed was 1,006km/hr (625mph), and the coast-to-coast crossing took 2hr 59min 30sec.

After much practice Short Brothers test pilots had mastered the S.C.1, and on October 25 the first free hovering flight away from the tethering gantry was made at Sydenham, Belfast. Chief test pilot Tom Brooke-Smith hovered the aircraft at 30ft and "made tentative probes in the horizontal plane before alighting". Full transition was in sight. By the end of the year excursions away from the gridded platform were normal procedure.

Late in the year the Soviet Union came forward to claim two records for height with payload with the Ilyushin Il-18 turboprop-powered passenger transport. On November 14 an altitude of 12,471km (40,915ft) with a 15,000kg (33,069lb) load was reached, and the following day 13,154m (43,156ft) was attained carrying 10,000kg (22,046lb). Captain for both flights was Vladimir Kokkinaki.

Can Harrier go Supersonic?

Steve Broadbent

An early AV-8B Harrier II carrying a load of bombs. Much improved but still subsonic, this latest Harrier version could finally demonstrate the virtues of V/Stol and encourage development of a supersonic successor. (BAe)

Few combat aircraft can have had such a stormy and protracted development as the Harrier. Popularly dubbed the "jump jet," the Hawker P.1127, as the Harrier was originally known, was born at a most unfortunate moment in British aviation history. During 1957 the government of the day had published a White Paper — known as the "Sandys White Paper" after the Defence Minister who was then in office — which declared that there was no longer a place for manned combat aircraft and that their tasks could all be performed by missiles. The immediate result was the cancellation of advanced aircraft like the supersonic eight-engined Avro 730, work on which had reached the mock-up stage at the A.V.Roe factory in Manchester, and the development of guided and nuclear weapons. That year the minds of the services and the government were very much turned away from fighters, let alone a proposal as revolutionary as the P.1127.

During the summer of 1957 two of the last great men of the British aircraft industry — Dr (later Sir) Stanley Hooker, then technical director of Bristol Aero Engines, and Sir Sidney Camm, chief designer of Hawker Aircraft — began a series of meetings to explore the possibility of developing a British vertical/short take-off and landing (V/Stol) fighter. The idea was not entirely new, for while the origin of the V/Stol concept is lost in aviation legend, the first practical step on the road which eventually led to Harrier was a proposal put to Bristol Engines in 1956 by a Frenchman, Michel Wibault. He suggested a "ground attack gyropter" based on a Bristol Orion turboprop driving four centrifugal blowers, the casings of which could be rotated through 90°. This method of redirecting the engine exhaust jet remains the core of the Harrier concept to the present day.

Wibault's idea was not entirely practical, but it did capture the imagination of the designers at Bristol. The Orion turboprop was replaced by a much lighter jet engine, the BE.48. This too gave rise to engineering

153

problems, so the BE.52, a development of the Orpheus turbojet, was adopted. This became the BE.53, then the BE 53/2, which was renamed Pegasus 1 as the project with Hawker developed.

Hooker had taken Wibault's ideas and the Bristol developments to Camm at Kingston, and the two teams jointly designed the P.1127 at what today seems a very rapid pace indeed. The first full discussions between the two companies took place in the summer of 1957 and the Pegasus was installed in a P.1127 airframe just three years later. An indication of the way aerospace development goes is the fact that the first Pegasus 1, which ran in September 1959, had a thrust of 9,000lb; the flight-rated Pegasus 2 had a thrust of 12,000lb (but a V/Stol life of only 15hr), while the latest Pegasus proposal, the 11-35, has a thrust around 24,000lb and a life of 1,000hr.

But despite their enthusiasm the two companies still had to overcome the Sandys White Paper thinking which now pervaded the Ministry of Defence and the services. A new conventional fighter would have had a hard time winning acceptance; something as revolutio-hard time winning acceptance; something as revolution-ary as V/Stol was almost out of the question. The P.1127 was rescued largely by the Americans, who agreed to pay 75 per cent of the engine development costs through the Mutual Weapons Development Programme Agency. The aircraft itself became the subject of a Nato specification designed to generate a need for V/Stol.

Wind-tunnel testing was carried out in the USA in 1958 and Hawker was just about to commit itself to the building of a prototype as a private venture when, at last, the Ministry of Supply ordered two prototypes late in 1959. The first tethered flight took place on October 21, 1960. Several prototype aircraft embarked on trials, but still there was no firm programme from the Ministry of Defence. Eventually, however, a British-German-American trinational evaluation of the P.1127 — now called Kestrel — began in 1965.

Supersonic capability had always been on the cards for the project: Bristol Engines was gaining experience with the Olympus destined for Concorde, and the Kingston office had been knocking on the supersonic door for some years with Hunter developments. Indeed, the P.1127 itself had gone supersonic in a shallow dive on December 12, 1961. Then there was the urgent need to keep up with Kingston's arch-rival, the English Electric design office at Warton, which still had Britain's only production supersonic aircraft, the Lightning, and a lion's share of the prestigious TSR.2.

The P.1154, the Mach 2 development of the P.1127, was to be powered by the BE.100 engine. Based on the Pegasus but significantly larger, the BE.100 featured plenum chamber burning (PCB)). Under this method of increasing the thrust of a vectored-thrust turbofan to permit supersonic flight, air from the fan is burned in a

Above: **AV-8A Harrier of US Marine Corps squadron VMA-231. Despite an initially high accident rate—due in part to a policy of assigning first-tour pilots to fly a uniquely demanding aircraft—the Marines are about to become the world's leading V/Stol exponents.** (BAe)

Right: **Royal Navy Sea Harrier FRS1 seen during trials aboard HMS** Hermes. **The FRS1 was the first Harrier variant to enter combat, performing to devastating effect against supersonic opposition in the Falklands War.** (BAe)

type of combustor known as a plenum chamber before being exhausted through one of the two pairs of rotating nozzles.

1965 was a critical year for the Harrier project. The trinational squadron was working up at West Raynham, the P.1154 supersonic programme was going ahead and there were signs that people were beginning to understand the notion of a V/Stol fighter. The Sandys doctrine of eight years earlier was forgotten and fighters were back on the "acceptable" list at Whitehall and Westminster. Then, on February 2, the bombshell burst. Prime Minister Harold Wilson

announced that the P.1154 was to be cancelled (along with other aircraft projects: TSR.2 followed four months later). The P.1154 had been intended to replace the Royal Navy's Sea Vixens and the RAF's Hunters but the two services could not agree on a specification which was common enough to permit economical production and the RN had selected the Phantom in favour of the P.1154(RN) in 1964. The RAF had gone ahead with its own variant and contruction of a prototype had started at Kingston. Now the RAF was to have Phantoms (and eventually Jaguars) to replace its Hunters.

There was a small sop to Hawker Siddeley and Bristol Siddeley (as Hawker and Bristol Aero Engines had become) in the form of a declaration that there was now "an urgent need for an operational version of the P.1127". Moves were made to order further development aircraft, leading to the formation of the first RAF squadron of Harriers (as the production aircraft was named) on April 1, 1969. The cancellation of the supersonic programme was a tremendous blow to the two factories at Bristol and Kingston, and to the British aerospace industry as a whole, which lost virtually all its advanced projects. Nevertheless, the BS.100 supersonic engine had completed over 600hr of PCB running on the test stand at Bristol and demonstrated a 35 per cent increase in thrust over the non-PCB engine. Fertile seeds had been sown for the future.

The Harrier then took the stage, and the supersonic effort, though not forgotten, was shelved for the time being. The Harrier GR1 was the standard RAF version and the US Marine Corps (USMC) ordered the Mk 50, designated the AV-8A in the USA. The GR3 is the Mk 1 retrofitted with the more powerful Pegasus 103, and the T2 and T4 are the corresponding two-seat variants, which can be used for both flying and weapons training. Later, the Harrier joined the Navy as the FRS1 Sea Harrier, with revised cockpit and a Pegasus 104 engine. The P.1127 had first landed on board ship as early as February 8, 1963, but it was 1977 before the Sea Harrier was ordered. The exploits of that aircraft and its RAF cousin during 1982's Falklands War brought the jump-jet firmly before the public eye. Not that it had ever really wanted for publicity: throughout the life of the project the manufacturers have used air shows and air races to demonstrate the Harrier's unique capabilities. The biggest publicity coup of all came with the dramatic though unplanned landing of a Sea Harrier on board a Spanish ship in the Atlantic last June.

Out of the original USMC AV-8A came a requirement for a development with significantly increased performance, leading to the 1973 proposal designated "AV-16A" (indicating twice the capability of the AV-8A). Since then the large-scale development of the Harrier concept has been in American hands. Britain declared that it had no real interest in "AV-16A" and

the Americans were left to work on it alone. The first stage was to convert two AV-8As to YAV-8Bs (AV-8B being the official designation for the AV-16A proposal), and the prototype flew late in 1978.

A British requirement for an advanced Harrier was developing in parallel and the two lines of thought came together in 1981 with the announcement of the AV-8B/GR5 joint American-British programme, under which McDonnell Douglas will build about 60 per cent of each aircraft and British Aerospace at Kingston the rest. Rolls-Royce at Bristol and Pratt & Whitney in America share the engine work. The USMC plans to operate 336 AV-8Bs while the RAF will get 60 similar GR5 Harriers. Spain has also ordered 12 AV-8Bs to supplement its AV-8S Matadors already in service. Future Harrier development therefore depends on this programme, an update of the Sea Harrier and the re-emergence of supersonic V/Stol.

By early 1983 the first AV-8Bs had already proved their capabilities in tests from the US Naval Test Centre at Patuxent River in Maryland. In one trial seven 570lb bombs were dropped on a target 366nm from base, after which the aircraft returned at 42,000ft. At the end of the mission 800lb of fuel remained; no external fuel was carried. On a second, low-level, mission the aircraft dropped twelve 530lb bombs 160nm from base, having loitered at low level for nearly an hour. This represents a huge improvement on the original P.1127, but then there has been over 20 years of development work on both sides of the Atlantic.

The AV-8B and GR5 are together known as Harrier

Above: **An AV-8B lands, kicking up the familiar cloud of dust. This could be a problem if re-ingested by the engine.** (*McDonnell Douglas*)

Left: **An AV-8B dropping a stick of 530lb bombs.** (*McDonnell Douglas*)

II, which, although superficially similar to the original Kestrel and Harrier, is almost completely different beneath the surface. Most obvious identification features of the new variant are the raised cockpit, enlarged canopy and, in comparison with the GR3, the lack of the extended nose which houses the Ferranti laser system. The raised cockpit gives better pilot vision and provides more space for avionics. Falklands experience suggests that a radar might be incorporated in the RAF's Harrier IIs and in versions offered for export. At the moment the USMC (which flies the American Harriers) wants a radar, but the Navy (which holds the pursestrings) doesn't. Whatever the outcome, the existing nose profile is large enough to take a radar.

Under the canopy the Harrier II is a big improvement on the earlier versions, which are said to call for some piano-playing expertise, such is the multitude of small switches and buttons. Harrier II has digital electronics and the cockpit includes a large, multi-function display which gives weapon-aiming and navigational data. In the RAF version there will also be

Above: **An AV-8B in the new low-visibility paint scheme.** (*McDonnell Douglas*).

Below: **An AV-8B shows off its underfuselage strakes and fence (which provide extra lift in the hover), the leading-edge root extension and large flaps.** (*McDonnell Douglas*)

The third Full Scale Development AV-8B carrying bombs and extra fuel tanks. (*McDonnell Douglas*)

a large moving map to show the pilot exactly where he is as the flight progresses. The modern head-up display common to both versions presents the pilot with vital information while he keeps watch out of the cockpit. Unfortunately, there is little British equipment on board even the RAF's Harrier IIs, a reminder that the project has largely crossed the Atlantic. With the USMC buying most of the aircraft, it is not cost-effective to specify British avionics for the RAF aircraft.

The Harrier II is the first production combat aircraft to embody a large proportion of composite materials, which are light in weight, durable and highly damage and fatigue-resistant, will not corrode and are easy to repair. Some 26 per cent of the aircraft's structural weight is graphite epoxy, resulting in a weight saving of 480lb (218 kg) over a similar structure made with conventional materials. Every pound saved in a V/Stol fighter is another pound of armament that can be carried, and weight saving is even more vital than in a conventional aircraft.

Externally there are a number of subtle changes from the GR3/AV-8A. The wing has a greater span, giving an extra 29ft² of area, and a new, supercritical aerofoil section which gives less drag as the aircraft approaches the speed of sound. Larger flaps improve short take-off performance, while underfuselage strake and a retractable forward fence help improve Vtol capability by 1,200lb. Manoeuvrability is improved by a wing leading-edge extension, pioneered on earlier Harrier submissions by British Aerospace.

The Pegasus engine, too, has changed since the days of Harrier GR1. In Harrier II a new intake with an elliptical profile and double auxiliary doors improves Vtol peformance by a further 600lb. The Pegasus 11-21E, with a thrust of 22,000lb, will be the standard engine. The improvements over the Pegasus 11 in the GR3 are mainly concerned with reliability, but the new engine also incorporates such technical tongue-twisters as a "triple interstage labyrinth" and better HP turbine cooling and sealing. Rolls-Royce is proposing a further variant, the Pegasus 11-35, for future Harrier IIs. The 11-35 has a front fan capable of handling an increased mass flow, and gives an extra 1,200lb of thrust compared with the 11-21E.

Four Full Scale Development AV-8Bs are in flight test at Paxutent River and at Edwards Air Force Base, California; they will be followed by 12 pilot production aircraft starting at the end of 1983. Initial operational service with the USMC is scheduled for 1985. Metal-cutting on the RAF's first four GR5s (three development aircraft and the first production aircraft) began in the middle of 1983; first flight is due in 1985 and squadron service in 1987. Among the USMC's 336 Harrier IIs could be several two-seat TAV-8Bs, so we may well see an RAF T6. Meanwhile, the 47 AV-8As which are being updated by the Marine Corps at Cherry Point NAS, North Carolina, with modern avionics and the AV-8B's lift improvement devices are designated AV-8C.

The Falklands War did a lot to convince doubters of the operational capabilities of the Harrier and led, among other things, to an update programme for the Sea Harrier, which is to have an improved radar and a radar-guided beyond-visual-range missile. Beyond that there is the proposed naval version of the Harrier II, the AV-8B+, which could augment the Sea Harriers of the Royal Navy in the 1990s.

For the past 15 years Rolls-Royce at Bristol has kept a watching brief on the possibilities of supersonic V/Stol. When the BS.100 project was cancelled in 1965 there were still some technical problems to be overcome, but there can be no doubt that the engine had run successfully. In 1979, under a small government contract, Rolls-Royce at Bristol revived its PCB programme. Since then a new test facility has been established by Rolls-Royce and the Ministry of Defence on part of the Shoeburyness range in Essex.

Initial tests, in 1980, involved an early Pegasus 2 fitted with PCB and housed in a test stand at Shoeburyness: 17hr of engine running included investigations of water ingestion and intake distortion. Following this phase the engine was run in a high-altitude test facility at the National Gas Turbine Establishment, Pyestock, where the high-altitude, low-speed end of the envelope was explored to ensure that PCB would function in all flight conditions.

For Phase 3 an old Harrier airframe is being suspended from a gantry so that it can be moved about all three axes for tests at differing angles of roll, pitch and yaw. The object is to devise techniques which will prevent hot PCB gases from being re-ingested, and avoid overheating the fuselage. These trials started in the autumn of 1983 and will continue for about a year.

The original BS.100 engine was markedly bigger than the Pegasus and had PCB designed into it from scratch; these latest tests are the first to be carried out on a Pegasus. To give some idea of the problems that arise with plenum chamber burning, the temperature of the exhaust gases at the exit from the nozzle is 2,100°F, compared with just 234°F without PCB. This high temperature has obvious consequences for the nearby airframe and the take-off surface (particularly on a carrier, with its crowded metal deck). The hot exhaust gases must also be prevented from being re-ingested through the main intake, which could lead to a significant loss of thrust.

Visible on the underside of this AV-8B are the seven weapon hardpoints and underfuselage cannon pods. (*McDonnell Douglas*)

Above: **PCB Pegasus running on the test stand.**
(*Rolls-Royce*)

Right: **Design studies of an advanced V/Stol type for the US Navy. Note the two different varieties of supersonic intake and the impressive sensor and weapon fit.** (*Rolls-Royce*)

The future of both PCB and supersonic V/Stol rests with the British and American defence authorities and the three companies which have been co-operating for so long: British Aerospace, Rolls-Royce and McDonnell Douglas. The next phase would be airborne testing of a PCB Pegasus. Some trials could be carried out with a Harrier airframe suitably modified to correct for the differing centre of thrust, but a full test in a new airframe would also be needed and would be extremely expensive. Although the current work is being done with old Pegasus 2 engines, the results are directly applicable to the Pegasus 11 of the Harrier GR3 and GR5, in which the thrust would be increased from around 22,000lb to 31,000lb or beyond. This is greater than the output obtained from the larger BS.100 in 1965.

Pegasus and Harrier are both getting a little long in the tooth and must be nearing their development limits. The Pegasus has been largely confined in physical size by the Harrier fuselage, and a brand-new engine designed to combine everything learned on Pegasus with the latest military powerplant technology would have a better thrust: weight ratio (vital in V/Stol) and improved economics of operation. Rolls-Royce has on the drawing board ideas for a Pegasus successor rated at 30,000lb (dry) and 45,000lb (PCB) which would suit a supersonic V/Stol fighter from BAe or McDonnell Douglas for service in the next decade; both companies are testing such designs in the wind

tunnel. Only political will and finance are needed to bring about a supersonic successor to the Harrier some 30 years after P.1154 was cancelled.

With the operational potential of such an aircraft becoming plain, and the necessary technology currently being proved, there seems to be every chance that the 1990s could see a brand-new V/Stol airframe on the lines of those illustrated and employing one or even two PCB engines, either Pegasus developments or all-new units. And the direct ancestor of this aircraft is a design that today, nearly 25 years after those first meetings between Stanley Hooker and Sidney Camm, is still the world's only operational fixed-wing V/Stol combat aircraft, in spite of dozens of attempts to equal or better it.

Air transport pulls out of the dive

Chris Kjelgaard

In the last three years the nature of the world's air transport industry has changed. The airlines have become commercially cautious as never before, and never again will a single manufacturer embark speculatively on a new airliner programme: the development costs are too great and the risks too high.

The first three years of the 1980s saw the world's major airlines lose more money than ever before. The lengthy world recession had caused the traffic of the big Western carriers to fall off alarmingly and their problems were compounded by the new aircraft they had ordered in the late 1970s, when all their traffic predictions showed continuing healthy growth. There is now general agreement that the recession has eased and that things will get better again for the airlines. They are all set to make hay while the sun shines, having become leaner and more efficient to survive the recession. As things continue to improve, the airlines will make big profits: they now carry at least as many passengers as they used to, but with fewer staff and aircraft, and at less cost to themselves.

What is good for the airlines is not necessarily good

Above: **Braniff International's collapse in early 1982 sent tremors through the Western airline industry. Many observers saw it as the forerunner of several similar bankruptcies among large US carriers. But then most of the big operators managed to cut their costs, and were further helped by a timely stabilisation in oil prices.** (*Boeing*)

for the manufacturers, however. The aircraft builders like to see the airlines make money, because then they can order new equipment. But their sufferings in the recession have made the carriers extremely cautious about ordering new airliners in response to growth predictions that might prove dangerously wrong. Two major airlines, Laker and Braniff, died during the last three years, and many more — Pan Am, Air Florida and Eastern Air Lines among them — nearly went the same way. The two casualties had embarked on ambitious fleet expansion programmes just as the recession started, and there can be no doubt that this contributed to their demise.

Commercial caution apart, the airlines lost so much money in the early 1980s that they cannot afford many new aircraft over the next few years. And they still have excess capacity in the form of the new aircraft ordered late in the 1970s to cope with the predicted extra traffic which failed to materialise.

Unfortunately for the manufacturers, just as the airlines were losing more and more money their products were becoming more and more expensive. Inflation was partly to blame, but there was another reason. During the recession the planemakers reacted to continuously rising oil prices by setting out at great expense to cut fuel consumption. At the same time, the companies which build the big turbofans — Pratt & Whitney, General Electric and Rolls-Royce — embarked on hugely expensive new programmes and sought to make large fuel-burn improvements in their existing powerplants. All this research and development investment was passed on to the customer, and as aircraft became more expensive the airlines became less able to buy. At the same time, the more money they lost the more they needed the new aircraft for their lower fuel costs.

This classic vicious circle may now have been broken by the stabilisation of oil prices in the last year or so. This unexpected relief came after ten years in which the airlines saw fuel costs rise as a proportion of their total expenses from about 6 or 7 per cent to well over 30 per cent.

The outcome of all this is that the manufacturers are offering technologically superb aircraft to an air transport industry which is unwilling to take the plunge, for two reasons. First is the high purchase cost of the new generation of airliners, something the manufacturers can remedy with attractive financing terms and gov-

Below: **The brand-new PW2037 is Pratt & Whitney's competitor to the RB.211-535 as a Boeing 757 powerplant. Much of the technology developed for the 2037 is being incorporated into the new and very powerful PW4000, designed for the 747 and the big widebodies.** (*Pratt & Whitney*)

Bottom: **The Airbus A310 was one of three new digital-flightdeck airliners to enter service early in 1983. The order book for the A310 grew only slowly after healthy initial purchases: many carriers saw it as too big and expensive to replace their current equipment in the short term.** (*Airbus*)

ernment export loan support. But the second objection is harder to overcome: the carriers believe that the new types are simply too big. Having just survived the recession by the skin of their teeth, the operators no longer trust long-term traffic growth predictions. As a result, they are unwilling to replace aircraft which they know to be the right size for their current markets with aircraft twice the size, three times as expensive and not necessarily any cheaper to run.

The airlines also have to be careful not to do anything to upset their markets — by running fewer schedules with bigger aircraft rather than more with smaller, for example — because passenger demand is a volatile and unpredictable thing. Airlines have to be especially careful when they have competitors on their routes. On most business routes it is frequency of service rather than type of aircraft that sells an airline to the passenger.

Why then have the manufacturers produced aircraft that may not be what the market really wants? The answer is simple: it takes at least four years to get an airliner from drawing board to revenue service. No company — not even Boeing, renowned for its efficiency — can do it faster. The type of aircraft required at the start of an airliner programme may be very different from what is needed under the changed conditions prevailing four years later.

Four new jet airliners entered service in the nine months between late 1982 and mid-1983: the Boeing 767 and 757, the Airbus A310 and the British Aerospace 146. In no case did development and production start later than early 1980. At that time the industry still seemed set fair for expansion: traffic was good, strong

growth was predicted, the airlines were making money and the trade in new aircraft was brisk. Big new aircraft were wanted to replace 727s and DC-9s. Each of the three larger types — the A310, the 757 and the 767 — had a good initial order base, and it seemed that the order books would go on swelling.

So they did for a while. But by the latter half of 1982 it had become obvious that orders for the new aircraft had dried up completely as the recession started biting. There were no big orders for the 146. Both Airbus and Boeing had months in which cancellations and delivery

---

Below: **The British Aerospace 146 has had a tough time because of the recession and the fact that its strongest selling point may also be its weakest. Although it can operate from runways too short for other jet airliners, the cost and the complexity of its four engines may make it too expensive for many smaller airlines.** (BAe)

Above right: **The recession killed off the TriStar programme. Although many airlines regarded TriStar as the best of the first-generation widebodies, Lockheed could not afford to keep it in production in the hope that the market would pick up.** (Lockheed)

Right: **The DC-10 was kept alive in the recession only by a big US Air Force order for the KC-10A Extender tanker/transport derivative. USAF production will keep the line open until 1986, when production of the new MD-100 variant is expected to begin.** (McDonnell Douglas)

postponements exceeded new orders. Boeing didn't sell a 757 or a 767 for over a year. Only the success of the 737 programme kept the giant US company's finances looking healthy. Although orders for the new types had picked up a little by mid-1983, demand is still nothing like as firm as it used to be. The cost of new airliners will probably never allow carriers to order aircraft in such quantities as they did in the 1970s.

Apart from changing the pattern of airliner sales, the recession also put an end to the TriStar programme and almost killed off the DC-10. In the end Lockheed pulled out of the airliner business completely, and for a long time it looked as if McDonnell Douglas might make the same decision. But then many airlines suddenly realised that the fairly slow-selling DC-9 Super 80 — now known as the MD-80 — was exactly what they needed to see them through their lean times. McDonnell Douglas encouraged some of the largest and most important US carriers in this belief by giving them super-lenient short-term rental deals on large fleets of Super 80s. Boeing was forced to offer Delta the

same kind of terms on 737-200s to prevent a switch to the Super 80.

McDonnell Douglas's bold marketing strategy immediately began to pay off. Although there remains a chance that the manufacturer could end up with large numbers of ex-TWA and American Airlines Super 80s on its hands in a few years, other airlines promptly followed the lead of the big US operators. McDonnell Douglas received more orders for the Super 80 in 1982 than its two major competitors did for all of their aircraft combined, and the orders continued unabated well into 1983. Suddenly, instead of leaving the airliner business to Boeing and Airbus, McDonnell Douglas was right back in the fray — and winning.

What kinds of large new airliners can we expect to see in the next few years? In short, fewer completely new designs will be built in the next four or five years than ever before. The cost of developing a big new airliner and its engine is nowadays too great for any one company to bear. Nobody is quite sure how many airliners of brand-new design will be needed over the

heavyweight like the 747, but it can compete at the other end of the scale by building the smaller A320.

The A320 is likely to be the only completely new design to surface by the end of the decade. Boeing and McDonnell Douglas do have their own designs for the so-called 150-seat airliner — the 7-7 and the D-3300 respectively — but they will both need financial and production support from international partners (notably Japan).

The US manufacturers are however in the fortunate position of having existing aircraft which they can develop relatively cheaply. The DC-9 Super 80/MD-80 has already taken some of the short-term potential market for the A320 and other new 150-seaters, and it will continue to make inroads as it is further developed. Detail improvements, rather than further stretches, are all that is needed to make this possible. In the MD-83 variant McDonnell Douglas has already nearly doubled the range of the original Super 80. For the smaller end of the market the manufacturer has up its sleeve the "de-stretched" MD-90.

Boeing believes it can do the same with the 737. The stretched and re-engined 737-300 is already in production, and Boeing has a further stretch called the 737-400 in preparation to compete with the A320. Beyond even that is the 737-500, which would be a 737-400 fitted with the completely new engine designed specifically for the new generation of 150-seaters. An international consortium led by Rolls-Royce and Japan

next decade or so. The fragile state of the world air transport industry has persuaded the two big US manufacturers that their best course over the next few years is to offer low-development-cost derivatives of existing designs.

The exception to the rule is Airbus, which must increase its product range if it is to compete on equal terms with the two other manufacturers. Although there is no question that over the last few years Airbus has given Boeing a nasty scare, the US giant still dominates in the market because it offers a wide range of aircraft. Airbus will probably never produce an ultra-

Above: **The Boeing 767 was designed from the outset to be stretched or given increased take-off weight in response to market requirements.** *(Aeritalia)*

already has such an engine under development and running. Boeing would hope almost to destroy the short-term market for the A320 with these two aircraft. In the longer term, so the reasoning goes, it could then design a completely new aircraft to push the A320 out of the market. All this goes to explain why Boeing has come to dominate airliner manufacturing: the Seattle company always produces designs that can be stretched or given increased take-off weight (and hence more range) in response to market demand.

McDonnell Douglas also knows the secret — witness the DC-9 family — but the Boeing 767 is probably the best new example of this philosophy. The basic airframe has already been approved for higher take-off weights than those originally certificated, permitting the carriage of more fuel. A further weight increase will

result in two new versions: the very-long-range 767ER, with the basic dimensions of the 767-200, and the 767-300, an 18ft 4in stretch of the basic aircraft which can carry 40 more passengers. Further stretches are possible, says Boeing.

Queen of the Boeing fleet is of course the mighty 747. 1983 saw the service debut of the 747-300, the biggest and most expensive 747 variant yet. It is not clear whether Boeing originally designed the longer upper deck in order to carry more passengers or to cut down on drag. But the fact is that the extra upper cabin length makes the 747 aerodynamically more efficient, so that it burns less fuel while carrying more people.

Boeing does not see a market for an even bigger 747 until the mid-1990s at the earliest, and believes that the

Below: **The Boeing 747-300 is the biggest and most expensive 747 variant yet, retailing at about $100 million. The extra length of the upper deck results in less drag while allowing it to carry more passengers than the original 747.** *(Boeing)*

Above: **The MD-100 advanced variant of the DC-10 is now on offer to airlines. If enough orders are received soon, McDonnell Douglas could have the type ready to enter service in 1987. It has winglets and other aerodynamic improvements to cut down on drag and so reduce fuel burn. It will have an advanced digital flightdeck and is designed for two-pilot operation.** (*McDonnell Douglas*)

747-300 will be the biggest-selling variant until that time. But even then it may not go for another stretch, preferring instead to redesign the wing and flightdeck completely. With a new engine such as Pratt & Whitney's proposed PW4000, this would make the 747 much more aerodynamically efficient and fuel-thrifty than today's aircraft. But it would be a massively expensive programme, and each new 747 would cost hundreds of millions of dollars.

Although airliners are designed to accept increased take-off weights, the manufacturers strive constantly to find ways of reducing basic airframe weight. The lighter the basic aircraft, the more passengers, cargo and fuel it can carry for a given maximum take-off weight, or the less fuel it will burn for a given payload range.

Airbus Industrie believes it can lose about 1½ tons from the basic airframe weight of the A310-200 by using lighter materials, while Boeing actually managed to save more than a ton of structural weight in the 757 during the course of the development programme. Weight reductions will be incorporated into other Boeing types, notably the 747-300, throughout their development lives.

McDonnell Douglas is now offering an advanced long-range derivative of the DC-10 for delivery in 1987. This aircraft — the MD-100 — would replace current DC-10s, TriStars and 747-100s. Apart from having new engines, it would have an airframe 2,500lb lighter than that of the existing DC10.

How are these weight savings made? Some small reductions can be achieved by carefully paring down over-strong parts of the structure. But most of the savings come from the use of lighter materials. Airliners increasingly feature extremely light plastic materials stiffened with carbon fibre or man-made fibres. These "composite" materials are formed by cross-plying layers of fibre to build up basic strength, then soaking them in a plastic resin and baking them till hard. Before baking the sheets are very easy to bend and shape. Afterwards they are hard and much stronger than most metal alloys for the equivalent weight.

The various composites have different properties. For intance, carbon-fibre-reinforced plastic can withstand a lot of bending stress but is likely to shatter on impact. Plastic reinforced with the man-made fibre Kevlar is much more resistant to impact. Aircraft components are therefore formed from a variety of different composites to give the desired impact and stress resistance.

The application of advanced composite materials in aircraft is still in its infancy, and it will be some time before the major airworthiness authorities accept that they can safely be used for those aircraft structures which bear the heaviest loads. But even now many parts of the aircraft's body, wings, engine pods and tail assembly can be made from composites, and the resulting weight savings can run to several tons.

Lightweight materials can also be used in airliner interiors. Extremely strong but light seats can be made from composites, and tough, lightweight carpets from man-made fibres. New lightweight galley equipment and trolleys can be made from plastics and materials which derive their strength from a hollow honeycomb structure. Airframe components are also being made using honeycomb construction techniques.

But the metal companies are now fighting back with new advanced alloys. A British company, Alcan Aluminium, is the world leader in the development of a new family of extremely light but strong aluminium alloys known as lithium aluminiums. They score over composites because they are cheaper to produce and buy. Boeing in particular is very excited about the new alloy, declaring that it will use them extensively in its new designs.

Weight reductions will also be achieved on tomorrow's aircraft by means of a new and entirely unrelated area of technology: fly-by-wire controls (pioneered on Concorde) and "relaxed-stability" flying characteristics. If an airliner's aileron, elevator and rudder controls can be activated reliably and safely by means of electronic signals passed through thin wires, then the heavy metal cable control runs and hydraulic lines found in today's types can be eliminated. The same applies to engine controls.

The instantaneous control response provided by flightdeck computers and digital electronic signals will permit the production of aircraft which are not properly stable in flight. No human reflexes could cope with the extreme "twitchiness" of the relaxed-stability airliner, but automatic electronic inputs from computer-linked flight controls will constantly adjust the position of the aircraft's control surfaces to keep it flying perfectly normally. Such airliners will probably give a smoother ride than today's aircraft.

The relaxed-stability aircraft will be lighter because its tailplane will be smaller. For safety reasons today's airliner drops its nose — pitches down — in a stall because its centre of gravity is intentionally located well ahead of its centre of lift. Big tailplanes and elevators, set to exert a constant downward force and so to keep the nose up, counteract the tendency to pitch down in normal flight. Tomorrow's airliners will not be designed to pitch down in normal flight, and without constant automatic control input they would oscillate up and down continuously. This condition of relaxed stability — with the centre of gravity lying nearly at the centre of lift — is made possible by fly-by-wire and will permit the tailplane and elevators to be made much smaller, as less balancing force is needed.

It is almost certain that the Airbus A320 will have fly-by-wire primary control actuators and some degree of relaxed stability. And anything Airbus is contemplating seriously must also be crossing the minds of the other big manufacturers.

Part and parcel of the fly-by-wire concept is the computerised flightdeck, which has already become fact in the A310, the 767 and the 757. This in itself represents one of the biggest revolutions in airliner design. The advent of fully computerised flightdecks and TV-screen instrument displays has brought numerous advantages. Pilots agree that it has not only made their job easier but also more pleasurable. One of the major functions of the flightdeck computers is to monitor constantly the myriad electronic, hydraulic, air and power systems. This lets the pilots give more of their attention to flying the aircraft and complying with air traffic control requirements.

No longer faced with the multitude of dials found in previous airliners, crews can scan their basic instruments easily. The new screen displays can present as much or as little information as the pilots want, and because each has several different display modes it can give far more information than dials ever could. This includes highly accurate map-display information about the aircraft's position in relation to navigational beacons, cloud masses and geographical waypoints. The screens do not burden the pilots with irrelevant information, and in the event of an emergency they immediately flash up exactly what is wrong and — in the Airbus A310 — what the pilot should do about it.

Using the consoles and screens the pilots can punch in the exact route they wish to fly. The autopilot and autothrottle, directed by the computers, will then fly the aircraft exactly along that route, compensating for changes in wind speed and direction. Engine thrust is constantly adjusted so that the aircraft flies at the most fuel-efficient cruise speed, and the most efficient climb and descent profiles are calculated and flown. The pilots can of course override the computers whenever they want to.

The manufacturers are constantly working on secret improvements to their wing aerofoil sections in the search for greater efficiency. Less visible but just as important is the effort to cut fuel consumption directly by refining the powerplant. Modern turbofan engines already operate at up to 90 per cent of their theoretical maximum mechanical efficiency. But it is still well worthwhile trying to better that figure, since each one per cent increase in mechanical efficiency results in a three or four per cent reduction in fuel burn.

Two fruitful lines of research are directed at reducing the amount of air which escapes round the tips of the compressor blades, and getting the turbine blades to work at higher temperatures. The less air that is lost round the edges of the compressor blades, the bigger the pressure ratio between the front and back of the compressor, and the greater the thrust for a given amount of fuel. Increasing the working temperature of the engine has the same effect. Manufacturers are now trying to find heat-resistant ceramic materials with the flexibility of alloys with which to make turbine blades.

Ultimately, however, a new type of engine is likely to replace the turbofan as the airliner powerplant of the future. Called the propfan, it is basically a jet engine driving a large number of aerodynamically efficient "fan" propeller blades through a very light and strong gearbox. Such an engine will produce high speeds and low fuel burn — 20-30 per cent better than that of today's turbofans — but is still at least five years away. The gearbox technology is not yet available, and the very thin blades will have to be so strong that new materials will be needed. Cabin and exterior noise will also be a problem, with the unshielded blades rotating at about the speed of sound.

Above: **The latest RB.211-535 variant—the E4—is revolutionary in that the pod entirely covers the rear part of the engine. This increases its fuel-efficiency by preventing the bypass air from separating from the engine afterbody. Turbofan bypass air—which does not actually pass through the engine—produces up to 90 per cent of the thrust.** (*Rolls-Royce*)

The noise problem is especially significant in view of the new noise regulations that will probably be introduced in most Western countries from 1986. If they are enforced, many older jets will not be able to operate into those countries and may have to be withdrawn from service. Some airlines may get round this by re-engining their aircraft, but this will be expensive.

A major problem confronting the world's aeronautical authorities is that of the operation of twin-engined airliners on long trans-oceanic routes. Today's big turbofans are highly reliable: some have been known to run for 10,000hr or more without having to be removed from the aircraft for repair. But if a twin-engined aircraft did lose an engine over the middle of the Atlantic, for example, the problem would be much more serious than if it had happened on a TriStar, DC-10 or 747.

Though there are many important questions facing the world's air transport industry in the next few years, most of them are commercial rather than technological in nature. Airliner technology has reached the point where air transport is extremely safe and is unquestionably the most important means of long-distance travel. The air transport industry will continue to grow in the future. It is up to the manufacturers to give the operators the best aircraft for the job.

Aircraft like the Boeing 707 (above) may be forced out of service when new international noise regulations come into effect in 1986. Operators may however get round the problem by re-engining their aircraft at less cost than it would take to buy a new fleet. The stretched DC-8 (Below) has been the subject of a very successful re-engining programme with CFM56s, which cut down on noise and increase fuel efficiency markedly.